Down Easy

A cookbook for those with swallowing difficulties

Author

Judy Best

Editor

Liz Scott

Published by Judy Best Cookx, Henderson, NV 89012

Editor: Liz Scott

Cover Design By: Darko Bovan

Produced by: CreateSpace

Nutrition Facts from: The Living Cookbook ©

This publication is designed to provide accurate and authoritative information in regard to the subject matter covered. It is sold with the understanding that the publisher is not engaged in rendering professional services. If professional advice or other expert assistance is required, the services of a competent professional person should be sought.

ISBN-13: 987-0-9854231-0-0

ISBN-10: 905423102

Library of Congress Control Number: 2012907804

Publication Date: June 20, 2012

Table of Contents

The doctors had finished with my throat cancer treatments. I was alive but my body was ravaged from the chemotherapy and radiation. I hadn't swallowed anything, not even water, for over a month. My stomach tube was my link with life. I had no saliva, my cheeks stuck to my teeth, and my tongue stuck to the roof of my mouth. I had no ability to taste and couldn't smell anything. I could barely talk, forcing the words slowly through my injured vocal chords. I was in constant pain, taking narcotics every four hours and I had lost twenty percent of my weight.

It was time to start healing my body - but how? That's what this book is all about. It was written by my wife. She believes strongly that you are what you eat, that good nutrition is essential and that unprocessed whole foods are the best way to nurture your body. She is not a nutritionist. She is a Le Cordon Bleu graduate and cooking is her passion. What could a gourmet cook do for a former "foodie" who couldn't even swallow?

She coined a phrase: "Your taste buds are in training" and set out to get them whipped back into shape. It wasn't easy. Once my feeding tube was removed, she began preparing freshly squeezed juices, then smoothies for me every three or four hours. After a few weeks I was able to detect salt – small progress to be sure – but at least a few taste buds were working. Gradually she introduced solid foods. Poached eggs were a favorite that I clung to until she gently pushed me to try more challenging things.

Eventually I was able to detect sweet, then bitter. My healing process was not a gradual progression but rather erratic. One day I could partially taste a particular food but the following day it had no flavor at all. Sometimes my throat got raw and voice raspy after eating a food, yet the next day I had no problem eating it. Every day was trial and error and as a result my wife continually revised her food preparation techniques and recipes.

As the months passed she created a great variety of dishes, each carefully crafted from her hand-selected whole foods. A key discovery was that the foods had to be moist *internally*. Sauces and gravies, no matter how carefully prepared, weren't enough to help me cope with my swallowing problems. "Down Easy" became her motto and eventually the title of this book.

I am much better now. To be sure I still have difficulty swallowing some things. My taste buds are still in training and I'm not ready for the culinary Olympics yet. However I have resumed my daily exercises and have regained sufficient stamina to start playing tennis again. Those who meet me have no idea that my health was so compromised only a few months ago. How much of this is due to the wonderful food that my wife prepared for me? Who knows? But it surely didn't hurt me, and knowing that I was eating properly helped improve my mental state.

With gratitude and love,

George Linton

Introduction

This book has been a labor of love. It has spurred my creativity and caused me to explore completely new areas in the world of cuisine. Many of the recipes are adapted from my cookbook library, the internet and from many television programs by my favorite chefs and home cooks. Others are my creations. I was born in Hungary and spent my childhood there, so some of the recipes are unique to that culture. My main goal has been to prepare easy-to-swallow healthy fresh foods, to bring out their natural flavors and to focus on nourishing recipes that enhance weight gain.

This book has many easy-to-prepare recipes using relatively few ingredients and simple procedures to create appetizing meals the whole family can enjoy. The key to making food easy to swallow is that the ingredients must have *internal* moisture. For example chicken, turkey, veal, shrimp or steak are very difficult to swallow, but buttery fish such as sea bass, turbot, or sea scallops are much easier, especially if baked or cooked in parchment paper. Fruits, especially, avocados, mangos and papayas are desirable because of their high moisture content and smooth texture.

Most ingredients used in this book are organic and minimally processed, although I do use ready-made broths, frozen fruits and vegetables and in rare cases a few prepared items. The recipes contain very little refined white sugar, no corn syrup or other chemically altered foods or ingredients. My rule of thumb is that if an ingredient isn't fresh or contains difficult-to-pronounce chemicals then it should not be consumed.

Many people have sensitivity to wheat or have Celiac disease. Some of my recipes are gluten-free and I have annotated those. However each recipe ingredient that you use should be carefully checked to ensure that it meets the gluten-free criteria. For example many soy sauces are available containing wheat but only a wheat-free variety should be used. Always double check your ingredients and read product labels carefully.

Some of the recipes are easier to swallow than others. They have been ranked for ease of swallowing levels from zero to four and are explained in detail in the Down Easy Swallowing Levels Section. These levels are based upon my husband's swallowing capabilities. Other people will undoubtedly have different swallowing abilities. The levels are offered only as a general guideline to help you select appropriate recipes to start with.

A final point to remember is that not everything needs to be puréed into baby food-like consistency with bland taste and unappetizing appeal. Do keep challenging the swallowing process. After all, swallowing involves muscles, and muscles need to be exercised in order to get stronger. I sincerely hope that you will find all the recipes tasty and easy to swallow. I have enjoyed creating them.

Visit my website judybestcookx.com. It's "A Nook for Cooks" where you will find additional featured recipes, information about special tools and gadgets and other cookbooks that I have written.

Acknowledgements

My very special thanks to my husband George Linton. He tasted, as best he could, offered opinions on my recipes and provided continual support to help bring this book to fruition.

Thanks also to my sister Ildiko Belay for her assistance in trying some recipes and making other meaningful contributions.

I owe a great deal of thanks to my sister-in-law Barbara Kocher, a former teacher of English, who has reviewed these pages and given many recommendations for improvements in grammar, presentation style and consistency. She also contributed several recipes and provided moral support and words of encouragement to spur me on.

My cousin in Budapest, Judith Szirányi not only assisted with the Hungarian recipes but her unique insight and reassurance kept me going when the task looked much too big to tackle. Her encouragement and gentle nudging also helped me so many times when I despaired.

Special thanks to my editor Liz Scott who polished my prose and checked each recipe so carefully.

Finally, thanks to my friend Deborah Richard for her unwavering friendship and her important insights which helped refine the book.

When health is absent, wisdom cannot reveal itself, art cannot manifest, strength cannot be exerted, wealth is useless and reason is powerless."

Herophilies, 300 B.C.

Symbols and Their Meaning

 Suitable for airline travel

 Full size Blender

Cook's Recipe Notes

 Small blender or "Bullet"

 Food Processor

Down Easy Swallowing Phases

 Mini Food Processor

Gluten-free

 Immersion Blender

 Hand-held Mixer

This section resulted from our first airplane trip. We learned a lot and want to share what we discovered. If you have swallowing problems chances are you won't be able to eat airline food (if you even get any), and not many (if any) choices will be available once you clear security. The solution is to prepare your own food to take on your journey. The challenge may be getting the food past the security checkpoints.

The US TSA authorities told me that it is not so much the food, but gels, liquids and powders that are of concern. However you should be aware that different regulations and rules may be enforced at different airports and restrictions may vary from country to country. Here are some suggestions to consider:

- Obtain a letter from your doctor describing your condition and limitations. Always keep this with you.
- Foods that you prepare yourself are less likely to trigger a security alert. Put them in your own storage containers. Some recommendations are:
  - Smoked salmon - keeps well for several hours without refrigeration.
  - Egg salad - will keep safely for several hours.
  - Vegetables - cooked or raw, especially grape tomatoes, cucumbers and zucchini.
  - Apple sauce - don't forget to put it in your own storage container.
  - Fresh fruits - apples, bananas, cut up melon, papaya, mango, blueberries, grapes, etc.
  - Individual protein powder packets - they are light-weight, easy to prepare and come in many flavors.
- Empty a plastic juice container that has a large opening and a tight fitting screw lid. Once you are cleared through security, purchase bottled water and mix it with the protein powder.
- Make certain to adhere to food temperature safety. For example don't take foods with mayonnaise on long distance flights or foods that are likely to wilt or spoil and become unappetizing.
- Visit www.tsa.gov for additional information.

Here are a few suggested recipes:
- Blueberry Muffins – page 18
- Dates Stuffed & Wrapped – page 5
- Egg Salad – page 117
- Green "Bread" – page 19
- No-Cook Brownies – page 52
- Red Potatoes with Basil Vinaigrette – page 162
- Vegetable Frittata Muffins – page 22
- Zucchini Logs in Smoked Salmon – page 13

This is the symbol used on a recipe page to indicate that it's OK for travel.

Phase 0

No saliva is present and swallowing is just starting after removal of the feeding tube. This is where the juice extractor is used. (For more information see Kitchen Appliances, Gadgets & Useful Tools). You don't need to follow the recipes, just juice a combination of fruits and vegetables. The ones that work best are:

- Apples, carrots and celery
- Beets and carrots
- Cucumbers and apples
- Oranges and apples
- Pineapple and pears

Phase 1

Saliva is just beginning to come back but it is still very difficult to swallow at all. Hot cereals, smoothies and creamed soups with very mild flavors work the best. Here are a few appropriate recipes:

- Almond Vanilla Panna Cotta – page 42
- Banana Ice Cream – page 45
- Blue Cheese Soup – page 170
- Butternut Squash Soup – page 171
- Carrot-Coriander Creamy Soup – page 174
- Chilled Avocado Cream Soup – page 176
- Chilled Blueberry Summer Soup – page 177
- Letcho with Scrambled Eggs or Tofu – page 30
- Oat Bran Cereal with Apple Sauce – page 31
- Oyster-Brie Soup – page 183
- Raspberry Fool – page 56
- Floating Island - page 50

Phase 2

A bit more saliva is present and differentiation between salty and sweet begins. Tiny bites of foods that have high internal moisture can be swallowed. During this phase some softer foods can be incorporated such as:

- Blue Cheese Soufflé – page 148
- Celeriac Mash – page 151
- Crab Crème Brûlée – page 138
- Eggs in Onion Nest – page 25
- Kahlúamisu – page 51
- Mushroom Stroganoff – page 79
- Potato Főzelék – page 186
- Roasted Borscht – page 187
- White Bean Purée – page 163
- Zucchini Squash Főzelék – page 190

Phase 3

Saliva is more consistent but still varies day-to-day. More flavors can be sensed but only mild spices can be tolerated. Slightly larger bites can be chewed. Suggestions are to prepare some varieties of fish such as sea bass, salmon, and catfish, as well as large scallops, oysters and all varieties of cooked vegetables.

- Allium (Onion) Bisque – page 166
- Avocado Papaya Salad – page 113
- Cherry Clafouti – page 46
- Cioppino – page 136
- Mushroom & Cheese Quiche – page 77
- Stuffed Bells – page 88
- Ratatouille Pie – page 82
- Scallops in Salsa – page 145
- Tostada Hay Stacks – page 93

Phase 4

Saliva is present most of the time, more spices can be tolerated and normal sized bites can be taken. Some foods with less internal moisture can be used including beans, heartier greens, and dark meat chicken. Some dishes to try include:

- Apple Custard Pie – page 43
- Beaufort Cod – page 134
- Chicken in Orange Sauce – page 73
- Chicken Salsa – page 74
- Chocolate Cranberry Truffles – page 47
- Fish in Parchment – page 141
- Light Bolognese – page 105
- Meatballs, Beans & Greens Soup – page 181

A ttractively presented foods are appealing to most people, even those with swallowing problems. A large plate can be intimidating so I came up with new presentation ideas while reworking old favorites into smaller portions.

Cottage Cheese – Pesto Stuffed Tomatoes (page 4)

Egg Salad in Romaine with Smoked Salmon (page 6)

Endive Spears with Lumpfish Caviar (page 7)

Zucchini Logs in Smoked Salmon (page 13)

I wrote this recipe while attending the Gourmet Cookery School in the early 1990's.

3/4	cup	free-range low-sodium chicken broth	1	large	garlic clove, minced
1/2	cup	red lentils, rinsed	1	tsp	dried basil
1 (14 oz)		can artichoke hearts in water drained, quartered	1/4	cup	dry red wine ,chicken broth or water
1/2	tsp	salt	1/2	cup	pecan pieces, finely chopped
1	Tbs	olive oil	2	Tbs	tamari soy sauce
1 medium		leek (white part only) halved lengthwise and thinly sliced	2	Tbs	cilantro, chopped

Procedure

1 Combine first 4 ingredients in a saucepan, bring to a boil, reduce heat, cover and simmer for about 15 minutes. Set aside and allow it to cool.

2 In a medium-size skillet, heat olive oil and sauté leeks and garlic until soft, 5 - 8 minutes. Add basil and freshly ground pepper.

3 Turn up the heat and deglaze with wine (broth or water). Boil until wine is absorbed.

4 Place lentil artichoke mixture, leek mixture and pecans in the bowl of a food processor fitted with a metal blade, add soy sauce and process until completely smooth. Add a bit more stock or water if the mixture seems too dry.

5 Add the chopped cilantro and pulse a few times to incorporate.

6 Scrape mixture into a bowl, cover and chill.

7 Serve with French baguette with crust removed & crackers (for those who can eat them), or sliced vegetables such as zucchini slices or bell pepper slices.

Servings: 8

Preparation Time: 30 minutes
Cooking Time: 25 minutes

Nutrition Facts

Serving size: 1/4 cup

Cook's Notes

Amount Per Serving	
Calories	127.95
Calories From Fat (46%)	59.23
	% Daily Value
Total Fat 6.97g	11%
Saturated Fat 0.71g	4%
Cholesterol 0mg	0%
Sodium 305.56mg	13%
Potassium 190.4mg	5%
Total Carbohydrates 11.99g	4%
Fiber 2.96g	12%
Sugar 0.82g	
Protein 4.61g	9%

This is from a French cookbook that I've had for years. The bottom of the artichoke is very moist. Stuffing it with mushrooms and goat cheese makes a lovely appetizer or side dish.

8 oz	button mushrooms		2	Tbs	finely chopped pecans
1 Tbs	butter		3	Tbs	grated Swiss cheese
2	shallots, finely chopped		1 (14.5 oz)		can artichoke bottoms, drained
2 oz	soft goat cheese				

Procedure

1 Preheat the oven to 400°. Lightly coat a baking sheet with cooking spray, or foil.

2 Wipe mushrooms clean and place in the bowl of a food processor fitted with a metal blade. Pulse until finely ground.

3 In a medium-size nonstick skillet, melt butter over medium heat. Cook shallots until soft, about 3minutes.

4 Raise heat to medium high and add mushrooms, sautéing for 5 - 8 minutes. Season with salt and freshly ground pepper to taste and remove from heat.

5 In a small bowl combine goat cheese and mushroom mixture. Add the pecans and half the Swiss cheese. Stir to combine well.

6 Divide mixture evenly among artichoke bottoms. Place on the prepared baking sheet and sprinkle with remaining cheese. Bake for 12 - 15 minutes or until lightly browned.

7 Serve warm as appetizers or as a side dish.

Servings: 6

Preparation Time: 30 minutes
Cooking Time: 15 minutes

Nutrition Facts

Serving size: 1 artichoke

Cook's Notes

Amount Per Serving	
Calories	177.01
Calories From Fat (34%)	60.32
	% Daily Value
Total Fat 6.95g	11%
Saturated Fat 3.51g	18%
Cholesterol 13.23mg	4%
Sodium 60.68mg	3%
Potassium 576.59mg	16%
Total Carbohydrates 24.03g	8%
Fiber 0.6g	2%
Sugar 0.98g	
Protein 7.56g	15%

Cottage Cheese - Pesto Stuffed Tomatoes

This is a wonderful combination that uses tomatoes as a serving cup. It is pictured on the back cover.

18		cherry tomatoes	1/4	tsp	lemon zest
1/4	cup	cottage cheese	Salt and freshly ground pepper to taste		
1	Tbs	prepared pesto sauce			

Procedure

1 With a sharp paring knife, cut off a tiny amount of the bottom of each tomato (to stand them up straight), then cut off 1/3 of the top of each tomato, scoop out the seeds and membranes and discard.

2 Using a paper towel, mop up any juices inside each tomato and set aside.

3 In a small mixing bowl combine remaining ingredients, adding salt and pepper to taste.

4 Fill tomato cavities with cottage cheese mixture and arrange on a serving plate. Garnish with a little parsley and serve.

Servings: 6

Preparation Time: 10 minutes

Nutrition Facts

Serving size: 3 tomatoes

Cook's Notes

Amount Per Serving	
Calories	110.09
Calories From Fat (12%)	13.07
	% Daily Value
Total Fat 1.65g	3%
Saturated Fat 0.1g	<1%
Cholesterol 0.94mg	<1%
Sodium 74.16mg	3%
Potassium 1096.35mg	31%
Total Carbohydrates 22.62g	8%
Fiber 5.22g	21%
Sugar 0.94g	
Protein 5.15g	10%

Dates Stuffed & Wrapped

This is such an easy finger food to make. The dates and cheese taste very good together. Be careful not to overcook them because the ham can become hard to swallow.

6	large	dates (preferably Medjool)		1/2	tsp	mustard (mild)
1	oz	manchego or cheddar cheese, cut into small logs		1/2	tsp	maple syrup
1	slice	(5/8 oz.) ham, rind removed cut into 1/2" strips				

Procedure

1. Stuff cheese logs into dates.
2. Mix mustard and maple syrup in a small bowl and spread a thin layer on each ham strip.
3. Wrap each cheese-stuffed date with the ham, place on a baking sheet seam side down (or secure with a tooth pick), and bake for 5 - 6 minutes until cheese melts and ham is heated through.
4. Arrange on a serving platter and serve warm or at room temperature.

Servings: 2
Yield: 6 stuffed dates

Preparation Time: 10 minutes

Nutrition Facts

Serving size: 3 dates

Cook's Notes

Amount Per Serving	
Calories	286.24
Calories From Fat (18%)	52.43
	% Daily Value
Total Fat 5.9g	9%
Saturated Fat 3.34g	17%
Cholesterol 23.64mg	8%
Sodium 441.55mg	18%
Potassium 583.95mg	17%
Total Carbohydrates 55.4g	18%
Fiber 4.86g	19%
Sugar 48.95g	
Protein 8.37g	17%

Egg Salad in Romaine with Smoked Salmon

This makes a lovely light lunch. It's one of our favorites.

| 1/3 | cup | egg salad (page 117) | 1 | oz | smoked salmon slices |
| 3 | large | romaine lettuce leaves | 4 - 6 | small | tomatoes, such as cherry or grape |

Procedure

1 Spoon prepared egg salad in lettuce leaves, top with bite-sized pieces of salmon and arrange on serving plate.

2 Add the small tomatoes and serve. Tomatoes may be warmed up slightly in a skillet if desired.

Servings: 1

Preparation Time: 10 minutes
Cooking Time: 15 minutes

Nutrition Facts

Serving size: 3 leaves

Cook's Notes

Amount Per Serving	
Calories	243.25
Calories From Fat (14%)	34.46
	% Daily Value
Total Fat 4.22g	6%
Saturated Fat 0.3g	2%
Cholesterol 6.52mg	2%
Sodium 657.63mg	27%
Potassium 2326.95mg	66%
Total Carbohydrates 45.54g	15%
Fiber 11.64g	47%
Sugar 1g	
Protein 13.89g	28%

This is another quick and easy finger food.

1		belgian endive
2	Tbs	creme fraiche (or sour cream)
1/2	tsp	lemon zest

1	2 oz.	jar white lumpfish caviar or salmon roe
1	tsp	chopped fresh dill sprigs
		Pimento-stuffed olives for serving

Procedure

1 Cut off root end of endive and separate leaves, arranging on a serving plate.

2 In a small bowl, mix crème fraîche, and lemon zest. .

3 Using a small spoon, scoop a bit of the crème fresh mixture on each endive spear, spoon a bit of lumpfish (or salmon roe) on top, decorate with the dill and serve chilled with the pimento-stuffed olives.

Servings: 2

Preparation Time: 10 minutes

Nutrition Facts

Serving size: 3 or 4 leaves

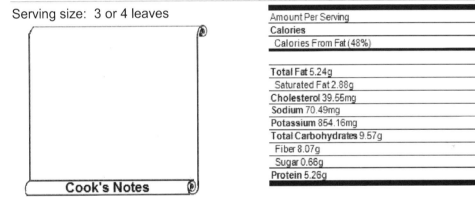

Cook's Notes

Amount Per Serving	
Calories	96.18
Calories From Fat (48%)	46.18
	% Daily Value
Total Fat 5.24g	8%
Saturated Fat 2.88g	14%
Cholesterol 39.55mg	13%
Sodium 70.49mg	3%
Potassium 854.16mg	24%
Total Carbohydrates 9.57g	3%
Fiber 8.07g	32%
Sugar 0.66g	
Protein 5.26g	11%

Kurzett Pâté

This Hungarian pâté, called Körözött is traditionally made with Liptauer sheep's milk cheese. To approximate the Liptauer cheese used in Hungary, I use soft goat cheese. Apparently, in aristocratic homes back in the day it was served topped with caviar!

4 oz	unsalted butter, softened	1/2	tsp	mustard (mild, yellow)
4 oz	cream cheese, softened	1/2	tsp	caraway seeds
4 oz	soft goat cheese	1/2	small	onion, grated
1 tsp	paprika (Hungarian sweet)	1/2	tsp	anchovy paste
		Chopped parsley for garnish		

Procedure

1. Place all ingredients in the bowl of a small food processor and mix until smooth, scraping the sides of the bowl if necessary.
2. Scoop into a serving bowl and decorate the top with chopped parsley and a sprinkle of paprika.

Servings: 8

Preparation Time: 15 minutes

Nutrition Facts

Serving size: 3 or 4 tablespoons

Cook's Notes

Amount Per Serving	
Calories	103.92
Calories From Fat (79%)	82.44
	% Daily Value
Total Fat 9.38g	14%
Saturated Fat 5.73g	29%
Cholesterol 26.14mg	9%
Sodium 111.07mg	5%
Potassium 43.83mg	1%
Total Carbohydrates 1.58g	<1%
Fiber 0.28g	1%
Sugar 0.91g	
Protein 3.71g	7%

Recipe Tips

In lieu of crackers and for easy swallowing, pipe (or spoon) small amounts onto thin zucchini slices cut on an angle.

This was inspired by P.F. Chang's and the Cheesecake Factory. Both make excellent Lettuce Cups and this is my easy-to-swallow version.

8	oz	baby bella mushrooms	1	Tbs	tamari soy sauce (or more to taste)
4		scallions, thinly sliced (white part and tips of light green part only), save darker green part for garnish	1 1/2	Tbs	hoisin sauce
			2	Tbs	rice vinegar, seasoned
			4	oz	(1/3 cup) canned water chestnuts, drained and minced
2	tsp	crushed garlic			
1/2	tsp	ginger juice (from grated fresh ginger)	2	Tbs	chopped cilantro
					Boston or butter leaf lettuce for serving

Procedure

1 Clean and trim mushrooms. Mince in a food processor by pulsing.

2 Heat a medium-size skillet, add mushrooms, scallions and garlic; sauté for a few minutes on medium heat stirring until mushrooms release their liquid.

3 In a small bowl, combine and mix remaining ingredients, except the water chestnuts and cilantro; pour over mushrooms and continue cooking for 5 - 10 minutes, until liquid is nearly absorbed by the mushrooms.

4 Add the water chestnuts and stir to combine. Remove from the heat and stir in cilantro.

5 Serve (warm or room temperature) in lettuce leaves.

Servings: 4

Preparation Time: 15 minutes
Cooking Time: 10 minutes

Nutrition Facts

Serving size: 1 lettuce leaf with ¼ mushroom mixture

Cook's Notes

Amount Per Serving	
Calories	58.68
Calories From Fat (5%)	2.91
	% Daily Value
Total Fat 0.4g	<1%
Saturated Fat 0.06g	<1%
Cholesterol 0.18mg	<1%
Sodium 361.86mg	15%
Potassium 782.55mg	22%
Total Carbohydrates 14.54g	5%
Fiber 1.69g	7%
Sugar 4.68g	
Protein 4.74g	9%

Pesto - Cheese Meat Balls ½

Combining ground pork and beef and adding cottage cheese to the mix makes the meatballs very tender.

1/2	lb	ground pork	1/2	cup	cooked couscous (plain or mushroom flavored)
1/2	lb	ground beef			
1/2	small	onion, grated	1/4	cup	prepared pesto sauce
2		garlic cloves, minced	1	large	egg, lightly beaten
1/2	cup	cottage cheese, drained	1/2	tsp	salt
1/4	cup	Pecorino Romano Cheese	1/4	tsp	freshly ground black pepper

Procedure

1 Preheat oven to 375°.

2 In a large bowl, combine all ingredients and mix with your hands until everything is incorporated evenly.

3 Form into walnut-size balls (use a small ice cream scoop or spoon).

4 Arrange meatballs on a baking sheet lined with foil which has been sprayed with cooking spray and bake for 35 - 40 minutes, until well browned.

5 Serve warm or at room temperature.

Servings: 6

Preparation Time: 30 minutes
Cooking Time: 35 minutes

Nutrition Facts

Serving size: 3 meatballs

Cook's Notes

Amount Per Serving	
Calories	321.84
Calories From Fat (62%)	200.91
	% Daily Value
Total Fat 22.22g	34%
Saturated Fat 9.81g	49%
Cholesterol 108.11mg	36%
Sodium 543.41mg	23%
Potassium 294.68mg	8%
Total Carbohydrates 6.01g	2%
Fiber 0.47g	2%
Sugar 1.47g	
Protein 23.09g	46%

Savory Dip

This seemingly simple dip has great flavor. Just steam and cool some vegetables and dip away.

1/4	cup	mayonnaise	1 tsp	Worcestershire sauce
1	Tbs	Dijon mustard	1 tsp	Maple syrup (or Agave Nectar)

Procedure

1 In a small bowl, whisk together all ingredients.

2 Chill until ready to serve. Pour into a decorative dipping bowl and serve with zucchini & peeled daikon radish rounds.

Servings: 4

Preparation Time: 5 minutes

Nutrition Facts

Serving size: about 1 Tbs

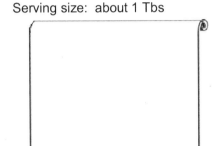

Cook's Notes

Amount Per Serving	
Calories	65.43
Calories From Fat (68%)	44.7
	% Daily Value
Total Fat 5.07g	8%
Saturated Fat 0.73g	4%
Cholesterol 3.82mg	1%
Sodium 163.83mg	7%
Potassium 19.75mg	<1%
Total Carbohydrates 5.12g	2%
Fiber 0.1g	<1%
Sugar 2.08g	
Protein 0.31g	<1%

Smoked Salmon Pâté

This is great for a party but can easily be cut in half. It's from the Three Rivers Cookbook which has been one of my favorites for as long as I can remember.

1 (16oz)		can salmon, drained and flaked	1	Tbs	lemon juice, freshly squeezed
8 oz		cream cheese (or neufchatel), softened	1	Tbs	liquid smoke
2	Tbs	grated onion	1	tsp	prepared horseradish
1/4	tsp	salt	1/4	tsp	Tabasco (optional)
			Chopped parsley for garnish		

Procedure

1 Place all ingredients, except the onions, in the bowl of a food processor fitted with a metal blade. Process until smooth, scraping down the sides if necessary.

2 Add grated onion and pulse several times to incorporate.

3 Scrape into a serving bowl, cover and chill until 30 minutes before serving. Garnish with the chopped parsley.

Servings: 18

Preparation Time: 10 minutes

Nutrition Facts

Serving size: ¼ cup

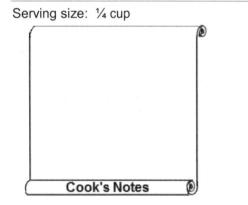

Cook's Notes

Amount Per Serving	
Calories	79.66
Calories From Fat (65%)	52.07

	% Daily Value
Total Fat 5.88g	9%
Saturated Fat 2.83g	14%
Cholesterol 27.73mg	9%
Sodium 225.3mg	9%
Potassium 102.88mg	3%
Total Carbohydrates 0.77g	<1%
Fiber 0.06g	<1%
Sugar 0.5g	
Protein 5.79g	12%

Recipe Tips

For additional flavor, zest the lemon before squeezing the juice, adding both to the mixture. Bring to room temperature before serving.

This is a terrific combination of flavors. Zucchini is naturally moist and when cut into tiny logs it is very easy to swallow.

3 oz smoked salmon (or lox)
2 Tbs Boursin cheese

1/2 small zucchini, cut into small logs

Procedure

1 Gently separate smoked salmon into strips, cut into 2 x 4-inch strips if necessary. Spread with a thin layer of Boursin, lay a couple of zucchini logs across salmon at one end and roll tightly.

2 Arrange rolls on a platter, seam side down, cover with plastic wrap and refrigerate until serving time.

Servings: 2

Preparation Time: 10 minutes

Nutrition Facts

Serving size: 2 to 3 logs

Cook's Notes

Amount Per Serving	
Calories	114.77
Calories From Fat (63%)	71.95
	% Daily Value
Total Fat 8.43g	13%
Saturated Fat 4.92g	25%
Cholesterol 27.28mg	9%
Sodium 952.86mg	40%
Potassium 151.41mg	4%
Total Carbohydrates 1.37g	<1%
Fiber 0.3g	1%
Sugar 0.74g	
Protein 9.13g	18%

Stuffed Eggs

This is a delicious version of deviled eggs. The smoked paprika gives them a great flavor. It originated from Emeril Lagasse.

8 large		hard-boiled eggs, cut in half, yolks removed
1/4	cup	mayonnaise
1	Tbs	extra-virgin olive oil
1	Tbs	scallions, thinly sliced (white part and tips of green part)
2	Tbs	chopped olives, black or green
1	Tbs	chopped pimientos
2	tsp	minced parsley
1	tsp	capers, drained
1/2	tsp	white wine vinegar
1/4	tsp	salt
1/4	tsp	smoked paprika
2 Tbs		tuna packed in olive oil (optional)

Procedure

1 Mash yolks together in a bowl using the back of a fork. Mix in all ingredients together, and combine well.

2 Put the mixture into a food storage bag, cut one corner and squeeze mixture into the cooked egg whites. Garnish with a sprinkle of smoked paprika.

Servings: 8
Yield: 16 halves

Preparation Time: 30 minutes

Nutrition Facts

Serving size: 2 egg halves

Cook's Notes

Amount Per Serving	
Calories	124.91
Calories From Fat (69%)	86.53
	% Daily Value
Total Fat 9.69g	15%
Saturated Fat 2.26g	11%
Cholesterol 188.41mg	63%
Sodium 216.35mg	9%
Potassium 72.96mg	2%
Total Carbohydrates 2.78g	<1%
Fiber 0.13g	<1%
Sugar 1.09g	
Protein 6.43g	13%

Caviar in Eggs

This is a decadent appetizer for special occasions.

6	large	hard boiled eggs, cut in half, yolks removed	1/2	tsp	mild mustard
					Salt and freshly ground pepper, to taste
1/4	cup	crème fraîche or sour cream	4	oz	caviar (black or red)
3	Tbs	chopped chives, more for garnish			
1		lemon, juiced			

Procedure

1 In a small bowl, mash the yolks, add remaining ingredients, except the salmon roe, and mix well.

2 Spoon mixture into the egg white halves or use a plastic food storage bag with one tip cut off and pipe mixture in.

3 Top with caviar, sprinkle with additional chopped chives and serve on a platter.

Servings: 6
Yield: 12 halves

Preparation Time: 15 minutes

Nutrition Facts

Serving size: 2 egg halves

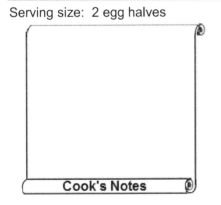

Cook's Notes

Amount Per Serving	
Calories	157.95
Calories From Fat (66%)	104.12
	% Daily Value
Total Fat 11.6g	18%
Saturated Fat 4.17g	21%
Cholesterol 306.55mg	102%
Sodium 350.07mg	15%
Potassium 123.6mg	4%
Total Carbohydrates 2.43g	<1%
Fiber 0.07g	<1%
Sugar 0.84g	
Protein 11.31g	23%

Zucchini Boursin Rolls

The zucchini strips get very tender and pliable. Be sure to cool them before layering on the cheese mixture.

3 small	zucchini thinly sliced, lengthwise	1 tsp	olive oil, or use oil from tomatoes
3 oz	Boursin cheese, room temperature	1 Tbs	finely chopped fresh basil
1 Tbs	sun-dried tomatoes in oil, drained, chopped, oil reserved		Salt & freshly ground pepper, to taste

Procedure

1 Preheat an oven broiler to high.

2 Grill zucchini strips in batches on a grill pan until brown and limp, 3 - 4 minutes per side. Remove to a cooling rack to keep from cooking further.

3 In a small bowl, mix Boursin, sun-dried tomatoes, oil, basil, and salt and pepper to taste.

4 Lay zucchini strips on a work surface and spread a thin layer of cheese mixture on each. Roll up gently and put them on a baking sheet lined with foil or parchment.

5 Broil rolls for about 1 minute until slightly brown on top.

6 Arrange on a platter and serve warm or at room temperature.

Servings: 4

Preparation Time: 10 minutes
Cooking Time: 8 minutes

Nutrition Facts

Serving size: about 4 rolls

Cook's Notes

Amount Per Serving	
Calories	112.37
Calories From Fat (80%)	89.97
	% Daily Value
Total Fat 10.64g	16%
Saturated Fat 6.61g	33%
Cholesterol 24.81mg	8%
Sodium 166.55mg	7%
Potassium 261.86mg	7%
Total Carbohydrates 3.88g	1%
Fiber 1g	4%
Sugar 2.53g	
Protein 2.63g	5%

I t is very difficult to eat bread when saliva is limited so I created the idea of green "bread", experimented a bit and came up with some new recipes. Pictured here is my green "bread" sandwich and a tostada made with corn "tortilla." The tortilla is soft and moist as are the toppings.

The blueberry muffin recipe is amazingly light. On a good saliva day my husband enjoys it with a little butter and jam. He was sometimes even able to taste the blueberries!

Tostada Hay Stacks (page 93)

Blueberry Muffins (page 18)

Green "Bread" (page19) makes a cool-looking sandwich

Blueberry Muffins

These muffins were inspired by Pam Whitmire. They are light and delicate and are very easy to swallow.

1	large	egg	1/2	cup	almond meal
1/2	cup	date palm sugar or brown sugar	1/4	tsp	salt
			1/4	tsp	baking soda
1/4	cup	safflower or canola oil	1/2	tsp	baking powder
1/4	tsp	vanilla extract	4 oz		sour cream or plain yogurt
1/4	tsp	almond extract (optional)	3/4	cup	fresh blueberries (or frozen, thawed)
1/2	cup	quinoa flour			

Procedure

1 Preheat oven to 400°.

2 In a large mixing bowl using a hand-held blender, beat egg gradually adding palm sugar. While beating, pour in oil slowly, add vanilla and almond extract if using, and set aside.

3 In a smaller bowl, combine flour, almond meal, salt, baking soda, and baking powder.

4 Combine dry ingredients with egg mixture and sour cream (or yogurt), alternating and mixing until just combined.

5 Very gently fold in blueberries, spoon into muffin cups, place on a small baking sheet and bake for 20 minutes or until a pick inserted in the center comes out clean. Cool on a rack.

Servings: 8
Yield: 8 muffins

Preparation Time: 15 minutes
Cooking Time: 20 minutes

Nutrition Facts

Serving size: 1 muffin

Cook's Notes

Amount Per Serving	
Calories	127.27
Calories From Fat (54%)	69.13
	% Daily Value
Total Fat 7.79g	12%
Saturated Fat 0.78g	4%
Cholesterol 24.17mg	8%
Sodium 162.72mg	7%
Potassium 55.19mg	2%
Total Carbohydrates 13.32g	4%
Fiber 0.45g	2%
Sugar 11.48g	
Protein 1.94g	4%

Recipe Tips

Use either paper or silicone liners in your 8 - cup muffin pan.

Green "Bread" ½

I borrowed this from Suzanne Somers' Fast & Easy cookbook. A sandwich is not out-of-the-question for the swallowing impaired when made with this "bread". It is soft and works well - especially while still warm and pliable.

10 oz	frozen chopped spinach, thawed and squeezed dry	1/4	tsp	garlic powder
4	large eggs, beaten			Salt and white pepper to taste

Procedure

1 Preheat oven to 400°.
2 In a medium-size bowl, combine spinach, eggs, and garlic powder, mixing until well combined.
3 Season with salt and white pepper.
4 Pour mixture into an 8 x 8-inch glass baking dish which has been sprayed with cooking spray and bake for 15 minutes. Allow to cool slightly before slicing into 4 equal parts to create 4 slices.

Servings: 4
Yield: 4 Slices

Preparation Time: 10 minutes
Cooking Time: 15 minutes

Nutrition Facts

Serving size: 1 slice

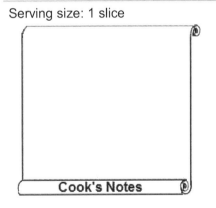

Cook's Notes

Amount Per Serving	
Calories	88.44
Calories From Fat (51%)	45.14
	% Daily Value
Total Fat 5.03g	8%
Saturated Fat 1.61g	8%
Cholesterol 186mg	62%
Sodium 127.11mg	5%
Potassium 466.79mg	13%
Total Carbohydrates 3.07g	1%
Fiber 1.58g	6%
Sugar 0.49g	
Protein 8.34g	17%

Carrot-Cranberry "Bread"

Spread it with your favorite jam or apple butter; top it with sliced fresh fruit such as bananas, pears, peaches, or kiwis, and enjoy it as a snack or a dessert. My husband likes it with warm maple syrup drizzled over the top.

2 cups	finely grated organic carrots	1	Tbs	honey or maple syrup
Pinch of salt		1/4	cup	dried cranberries (or raisins)
4 large	eggs , lightly beaten (or 3/4 cup egg whites)	1/4	tsp	vanilla extract

Procedure

1 Preheat oven to 400°. In a medium-size saucepan bring water to boil.

2 Add carrots and salt to boiling water, and blanch for a few minutes until carrots are tender. Drain and cool under cold running water and blot with paper towels to absorb excess moisture.

3 In a medium-size bowl, whisk eggs, carrots, honey, and dried cranberries (or raisins) until well combined.

4 Pour into an 8 x 8-inch glass baking dish which has been sprayed with cooking spray and bake for 15 minutes. Allow to cool before slicing into 4 equal slices.

Servings: 4
Yield: 4 Slices

Preparation Time: 10 minutes
Cooking Time: 15 minutes

Nutrition Facts

Serving size: 1 slice

Cook's Notes

Amount Per Serving	
Calories	280.57
Calories From Fat (2%)	6.34
	% Daily Value
Total Fat 0.72g	1%
Saturated Fat 0.02g	<1%
Cholesterol 0mg	0%
Sodium 735.14mg	31%
Potassium 707.17mg	20%
Total Carbohydrates 44.8g	15%
Fiber 3.96g	16%
Sugar 11.72g	
Protein 24.53g	49%

Recipe Tips

Use peeled organic carrots to make it easier. Use the fine grater disk on your food processor or box grater

Corn "Tortilla"

This is my very soft version of a corn tortilla.

1 (15 oz)	can corn, drained		1/4	tsp	ground cumin
3 large	eggs		1/4	tsp	salt
1/4 tsp	garlic powder		1/4	cup	sliced scallions

Procedure

1 Preheat oven to 400°. Spray 4 small pie tins with cooking spray and set aside.

2 Place all ingredients (except scallion greens) in a small blender and process on high for about 1 minute until smooth.

3 Divide equally between pie plates, scatter a few scallion greens on top of each and bake for 10 minutes. Allow to cool before using.

Servings: 4

Preparation Time: 10 minutes
Cooking Time: 10 minutes

Nutrition Facts

Serving size: 1 tortilla

Cook's Notes

Amount Per Serving	
Calories	89.97
Calories From Fat (40%)	35.66
	% Daily Value
Total Fat 3.99g	6%
Saturated Fat 1.25g	6%
Cholesterol 139.5mg	47%
Sodium 322.11mg	13%
Potassium 129.04mg	4%
Total Carbohydrates 8.64g	3%
Fiber 0.97g	4%
Sugar 1.54g	
Protein 5.96g	12%

21

Vegetable Frittata Muffins

These are great for air travel. Just pop them into a food storage bag and enjoy them at room temperature.

7 large eggs, lightly beaten		1	cup	chopped mushrooms	
1/2 cup	milk or unsweetened almond milk	1/2	cup	sliced scallions	
1 Tbs	unsalted butter	1/4	cup	chopped fresh tarragon or parsley	
1 cup	diced zucchini	1 tsp	salt		
1 cup	diced red pepper	1/2	tsp	freshly ground black pepper	

Procedure

1. Preheat oven to 350°. Coat a large muffin tin with non-stick cooking spray. Set aside.
2. In a 4 cup measuring cup, beat eggs and milk (or unsweetened almond milk) until combined. Set aside.
3. In a medium-size skillet, melt butter over medium heat. Add zucchini, red pepper, mushrooms, and scallions and sauté vegetables until soft, 5 - 6 minutes. Remove from heat and add tarragon (or parsley), salt and pepper. Fold vegetable mixture into egg mixture.
4. Fill muffin cups 3/4 full with mixture and bake 25 - 30 minutes until set and brown on top. Serve warm or at room temperature.

Servings: 8
Yield: 8 Muffins

Preparation Time: 30 minutes
Cooking Time: 20 minutes

Nutrition Facts

Serving size: 1 muffin

Cook's Notes

Amount Per Serving	
Calories	94.76
Calories From Fat (57%)	54.17
	% Daily Value
Total Fat 6.06g	9%
Saturated Fat 2.5g	13%
Cholesterol 167.79mg	56%
Sodium 377.03mg	16%
Potassium 214.47mg	6%
Total Carbohydrates 3.28g	1%
Fiber 0.77g	3%
Sugar 2.21g	
Protein 6.87g	14%

Thi is the easiest meal of the day. Honestly, my husband would have been happy with poached eggs every morning. He loves them. But to add a bit of variety I kept trying variations to get him to exercise his taste buds. On occasion I combined the poached eggs with hash browns or sautéed onions or smoked salmon or sliced ham. I also made a poached egg stack with avocado, tomato and green bread. Scrambled eggs placed inside a tomato was a fun variation as well. The porridges with apple sauce on top are also a favorite.

Green "Bread" Stack with Poached Egg (page 28)

Eggs in Onion Nest (page 25)

Quinoa Porridge with Apple Sauce (page 34)

Scrambled Eggs in Tomato Cups (page 35)

Cheesy Spinach Frittata

This is an excellent combination of flavors. The sun-dried tomatoes and fresh basil add a delightful taste.

4	large	eggs, beaten	2	Tbs	olive oil
1/2	cup	grated Parmigiano-Reggiano cheese	1/4	cup	finely chopped sweet onion (or scallions)
2		marinated sun-dried tomatoes, drained and cut into strips	10	oz	baby spinach (pre-washed)
4		fresh basil leaves, chopped or torn			Salt and freshly ground black pepper to taste

Procedure

1 Preheat oven to 450°.

2 In a medium-size bowl whisk the eggs, cheese and sun-dried tomatoes, add basil and salt and pepper to taste. Set aside.

3 In an 8" oven proof non-stick skillet, heat olive oil on medium-high heat. Add the onion, sprinkle on a bit of salt and sauté until soft, about 5 minutes.

4 Add the spinach and toss until the spinach wilts, about 2 minutes.

5 Increase heat to high and pour in the egg mixture. Stir everything together and cook until edges start to set, about 2 minutes.

6 Transfer skillet to oven and bake until it puffs and is brown on top, 10 -12 minutes.

7 Remove from the oven and allow to cool for a few minutes, then slide frittata to a work surface and cut into wedges.

8 Serve hot or at room temperature.

Servings: 4

Preparation Time: 15 minutes
Cooking Time: 12 minutes

Nutrition Facts

Serving size: 1/4 of frittata

Cook's Notes

Amount Per Serving	
Calories	208.04
Calories From Fat (66%)	136.56
	% Daily Value
Total Fat 15.4g	24%
Saturated Fat 4.71g	24%
Cholesterol 197mg	66%
Sodium 339.62mg	14%
Potassium 530.52mg	15%
Total Carbohydrates 4.95g	2%
Fiber 1.86g	7%
Sugar 1.4g	
Protein 13.38g	27%

The flavor of a sweet onion such as Vidalia or Maui is best but yellow or purple onions work too. The trick is to cook them slowly until they are soft and caramelized.

1 Tbs	unsalted butter	2 tsp	chopped fresh thyme leaves
1 Tbs	olive oil	4	eggs
1 large	red onion, thinly sliced		

Procedure

1. In a medium non-stick skillet heat the butter and olive oil. Sauté onions over medium-low heat until soft and brown, about 20 minutes.
2. Sprinkle with salt and pepper to taste, add thyme and sauté for a few additional minutes.
3. Make 4 holes or nests in the onions. Break an egg in each hole and cook, covered, on low heat to desired doneness.
4. Carefully arrange nests onto serving plates, sprinkle with paprika and serve.

Servings: 2

Preparation Time: 10 minutes
Cooking Time: 30 minutes

Nutrition Facts

Serving size: 2 nests

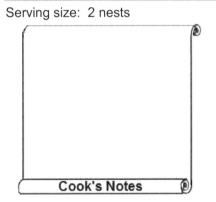

Cook's Notes

Amount Per Serving	
Calories	257.44
Calories From Fat (76%)	196.84
	% Daily Value
Total Fat 22.12g	34%
Saturated Fat 7.74g	39%
Cholesterol 387.27mg	129%
Sodium 143.69mg	6%
Potassium 151.17mg	4%
Total Carbohydrates 1.62g	<1%
Fiber 0.52g	2%
Sugar 0.4g	
Protein 12.75g	26%

Recipe Tips

Use any herb of choice such as tarragon, dill, cilantro, or parsley and serve with a couple of ham slices rolled up.

Fresh Figs in Syrup

Thanks to Claire Robinson for this delicious idea. You can serve this as a topping over oatmeal, ricotta cheese, cottage cheese, yogurt or even ice cream.

6   fresh figs
2 Tbs butter
2 Tbs agave syrup

Pinch of cinnamon
Pinch of salt

Procedure

1 Preheat oven to 400°
2 Wash figs, cut off the stem, cut in half and place cut side up in an oven-proof shallow dish.
3 Combine butter, agave, salt and cinnamon in a small saucepan over low heat. When butter has melted, stir well and drizzle over figs.
4 Bake for 10 minutes until figs are soft. Cool slightly before serving.

Servings: 4

Preparation Time: 10 minutes
Cooking Time: 10 minutes

Nutrition Facts

Serving size: 3 fig halves

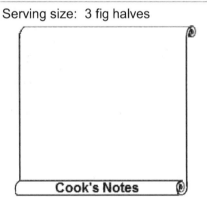

Cook's Notes

Amount Per Serving	
Calories	147.72
Calories From Fat (39%)	57.2
	% Daily Value
Total Fat 6.52g	10%
Saturated Fat 4.01g	20%
Cholesterol 17.1mg	6%
Sodium 95.86mg	4%
Potassium 296.41mg	8%
Total Carbohydrates 22.31g	7%
Fiber 2.82g	11%
Sugar 19.45g	
Protein 2.39g	5%

Recipe Tips

Use maple syrup or honey instead of agave, if preferred.

This is a soft and gooey open-faced sandwich. I like using Applegate Organics oval ham.

1	slice	Green "Bread"(page 19)	1 thin slice	5/8 oz. ham (rind removed)
1 1/2	Tbs	egg salad (page 117)	1 slice	muenster cheese

Procedure

1 Preheat an oven broiler.

2 Spoon egg salad on top of green "bread", top with ham and muenster cheese.

3 Broil for a few minutes until the cheese melts and serve.

Servings: 1

Preparation Time: 5 minutes
Cooking Time: 10 minutes

Nutrition Facts (excluding "bread" & egg salad)

One open-faced sandwich

Cook's Notes

Amount Per Serving	
Calories	247.49
Calories From Fat (43%)	105.48
	% Daily Value
Total Fat 11.91g	18%
Saturated Fat 6.24g	31%
Cholesterol 87.63mg	29%
Sodium 1606.84mg	67%
Potassium 913.67mg	26%
Total Carbohydrates 1.33g	<1%
Fiber 0g	0%
Sugar 0.31g	
Protein 32g	64%

Green "Bread" Stack with Poached Egg ⅓

This is pictured on the back cover. The Green "Bread" takes the place of the English muffin with a wink and a nod to the traditional Eggs Benedict.

2 slices	Green "Bread" (page 19)	3 Tbs	crab salad (page 139),
2	Tomato slices, broiled for a few minutes to warm	2 large	eggs poached (see RecipeTips)
2 slices	avocado, preferably Hass		

Procedure

1 Preheat oven to 275°.

2 With a 3 1/2" ring mold cut rounds from Green "Bread." Discard trimmings, top rounds with grilled tomato slices.

3 Cut avocado in half cross-wise, twist and pull apart, discard seed. Peel each half gently and cut in 1/4" thick rounds, place on top of tomato. (The center of the avocado should be a round hole where the seed used to be.)

4 Spoon crab salad inside the avocado hole. Using a spatula, place in the center of 2 serving plates. Keep warm in the oven while poaching the eggs.

To Assemble:

5 Remove Green Bread stacks from oven and gently arrange a poached egg on top of each.

6 Sprinkle top of eggs with a little paprika and serve.

Servings: 2 Preparation Time: 10 minutes Cooking Time: 5 minutes

Nutrition Facts

Serving size: 1 stack

Cook's Notes

Amount Per Serving	
Calories	529.14
Calories From Fat (53%)	279.03
	% Daily Value
Total Fat 32.97g	51%
Saturated Fat 5.63g	28%
Cholesterol 356.69mg	119%
Sodium 868.25mg	36%
Potassium 1724.79mg	49%
Total Carbohydrates 20.56g	7%
Fiber 13.39g	54%
Sugar 4.26g	
Protein 42.48g	85%

Recipe Tips

Fill a shallow pan with about 3 inches of water. Add 1 tablespoon vinegar and 1 teaspoon of salt, cover and bring to a boil. Uncover pan; turn heat down so bubbles barely break the surface. Crack eggs into a small bowl and gently drop into water one at a time. Simmer for 4 – 5 minutes and using a slotted spoon remove each egg to paper towels to absorb excess liquid.

Grilled Green "Bread" Sandwich

A cool-looking sandwich!

2 slices	Green Bread (page 19)	1 (1/4" thick) slice tomato, preferably heirloom
2 slices	muenster cheese, or cheese of choice	

Procedure

1 Place a slice of cheese on one slice of green "bread", top with tomato, add the second slice of cheese and top with another slice of green "bread". Lightly spray both sides with olive oil.

2 Heat a small non-stick skillet over medium heat and gently grill on both sides, being careful not to form a crust. Once flipped onto second side, place a lid on top, reduce the heat to low, and cook to melt cheese, about 2 minutes.

3 Remove from skillet, cut on a diagonal and serve.

Servings: 1

Preparation Time: 5 minutes
Cooking Time: 10 minutes

Nutrition Facts (excluding "bread")

Cook's Notes

Amount Per Serving	
Calories	107.24
Calories From Fat (69%)	74.41
	% Daily Value
Total Fat 8.48g	13%
Saturated Fat 5.36g	27%
Cholesterol 26.88mg	9%
Sodium 177.64mg	7%
Potassium 81.92mg	2%
Total Carbohydrates 1.24g	<1%
Fiber 0.22g	<1%
Sugar 0.31g	
Protein 6.72g	13%

This common Hungarian dish (spelled lecsó) can be served as a breakfast by adding lightly beaten eggs or crumbled tofu directly into the mixture. It can also be served on its own as a side dish, or even as a topping on toast. Roasted red peppers are used from a jar here due to their smooth texture, but any combination of bell peppers may be used. The most important thing is that the paprika be sweet and preferably Hungarian.

1	Tbs	olive oil or butter
1	small	onion, chopped, (about 1/4 cup)
1/2	tsp	salt
1/3	cup	sliced roasted peppers (about 1/2 of 7 oz jar),
1	Tbs	paprika (Hungarian sweet)
1 medium		tomato, chopped

1 cup crumbled medium tofu or 4 eggs lightly beaten
Freshly ground black pepper to taste

Procedure

1 In a medium skillet heat the butter or olive oil over medium heat. Add the onions, sprinkle with the salt and sauté until translucent. Add the sliced peppers and cook for a few minutes more, stirring until well combined.
2 Remove skillet from heat and stir in the paprika (see Recipe Tips)
3 Return skillet to the heat and add the tomatoes. Simmer gently until the tomatoes are soft, about 10 minutes.
4 Add the tofu or eggs and cook stirring gently about 5 minutes.

Servings: 2

Preparation Time: 15 minutes
Cooking Time: 15 minutes

Nutrition Facts

Serving size: about 1 cup

Cook's Notes

Amount Per Serving	
Calories	187.22
Calories From Fat (55%)	103.89
	% Daily Value
Total Fat 12.03g	19%
Saturated Fat 1.72g	9%
Cholesterol 0mg	0%
Sodium 600.78mg	25%
Potassium 548.29mg	16%
Total Carbohydrates 13.68g	5%
Fiber 3.79g	15%
Sugar 5.94g	
Protein 10.14g	20%

Recipe Tips

Paprika should always be added off heat because it burns easily.

Oat Bran is very easy on the throat, especially when topped with apple sauce. When I don't make my own, I like the 4 ounce individual portions – organic of course. They come in various flavors such as cinnamon, berry, etc.

1 large	apple (Braeburn, Pink Lady or other), cored, peeled & chopped	
1/2	cup	prune juice
1/4	tsp	cinnamon
3/4	cup	almond milk (organic, unsweetened)

1	Tbs	almond butter
1/4	cup	oat bran cereal
5	drops	stevia, cinnamon flavor (optional)
1/2	Tbs	honey (or agave syrup)

Procedure

1. In a small saucepan combine apples and 2 tablespoons of prune juice and simmer on medium low heat until apples are soft, about 5 minutes. Stir in the cinnamon and set aside to cool for about 5 minutes.

2. Place apples in a small food processor with 2 more tablespoons of prune juice and process until apple sauce consistency is reached. Set aside.

3. Combine almond milk with remaining prune juice, add almond butter, stevia, if using, and honey (or agave) on medium low heat and bring to a near boil, whisking occasionally until almond butter has melted.

4. Gradually whisk in the oat bran until incorporated. Whisk and continue to cook for about 5 minutes until liquid has absorbed into the cereal.

5. Pour into a serving bowl, top with the apple sauce.

Servings: 1

Preparation Time: 15 minutes
Cooking Time: 30 minutes

Nutrition Facts

Cook's Notes

Amount Per Serving	
Calories	407.45
Calories From Fat (27%)	111.28
	% Daily Value
Total Fat 12.78g	20%
Saturated Fat 0.94g	5%
Cholesterol 0mg	0%
Sodium 175.8mg	7%
Potassium 885.97mg	25%
Total Carbohydrates 70.32g	23%
Fiber 8.88g	36%
Sugar 45.48g	
Protein 7.41g	15%

Here is a version of oat bran cereal using store bought berry-flavored organic apple sauce.

1 cup coconut milk	1/4 cup	oat bran cereal
2 Tbs Spectrum ground flaxseed with mixed berries	1 (4 oz)	container apple sauce (organic berry flavor)
		Cinnamon for serving

Procedure

1 In a small saucepan, add coconut milk, flaxseed mix, and buckwheat groats, whisking to combine. Cook over low heat for 5 - 8 minutes until smooth and creamy.

2 Pour into a serving bowl, scoop apple sauce on top, sprinkle with a bit of cinnamon and serve.

Servings: 1

Cooking Time: 8 minutes

Nutrition Facts

Cook's Notes

Amount Per Serving	
Calories	340.29
Calories From Fat (38%)	128.55
	% Daily Value
Total Fat 14.9g	23%
Saturated Fat 0.33g	2%
Cholesterol 0mg	0%
Sodium 185.82mg	8%
Potassium 503.57mg	14%
Total Carbohydrates 55.06g	18%
Fiber 13.3g	53%
Sugar 25.25g	
Protein 10.48g	21%

The hash brown potatoes make a lovely bed for the rest of the toppings.

1	tsp	olive oil	2 large		eggs, poached (see Recipe Tips page 28)
1/2	cup	frozen hash brown potatoes	4 Tbs		prepared hollandaise sauce, warmed
2 slices		ham (5/8 oz. each cut into 3 1/2" rounds)	Paprika for serving		

Procedure

1 In a small non-stick skillet, cook potatoes gently until lightly brown.

To assemble

2 Place hash browns in the center of a serving plate, top with rounds of ham (overlapping), top with poached eggs and pour on the hollandaise sauce. Sprinkle with paprika and serve.

Servings: 1

Preparation Time: 15 minutes

Nutrition Facts

Cook's Notes

Amount Per Serving	
Calories	386.1
Calories From Fat (48%)	184.51
	% Daily Value
Total Fat 21.25g	33%
Saturated Fat 7.32g	37%
Cholesterol 408.47mg	136%
Sodium 1324.28mg	55%
Potassium 833.46mg	24%
Total Carbohydrates 23.35g	8%
Fiber 1.59g	6%
Sugar 0.37g	
Protein 26.47g	53%

Quinoa Porridge with Apple Sauce

This is an excellent breakfast. A delicious topping is Fresh Figs in Syrup (page 26).

1	cup	almond milk (organic, unsweetened)	1/4	tsp	vanilla extract
2	Tbs	Linwood flax seed cocoa blend	1		(4 oz) container apple sauce (organic cinnamon or berry flavor)
1/4	cup	quinoa flakes			Cinnamon for serving

Procedure

1 In a small saucepan bring almond milk to a simmer over medium heat, whisk in the flaxseed cocoa blend and quinoa flakes, and stir constantly until thick and creamy, about 5 minutes.

2 Remove from stove and stir in vanilla.

3 Pour into a serving bowl, scoop the apple sauce on top, and sprinkle with a bit of cinnamon to serve.

Servings: 1

Nutrition Facts

Cook's Notes

Amount Per Serving	
Calories	515.23
Calories From Fat (48%)	246.39
	% Daily Value
Total Fat 27.24g	42%
Saturated Fat 3.02g	15%
Cholesterol 0mg	0%
Sodium 205.38mg	9%
Potassium 370.56mg	11%
Total Carbohydrates 55.25g	18%
Fiber 20.28g	81%
Sugar 25.41g	
Protein 13.49g	27%

Be careful not to overcook the tomatoes or they may become too watery and mushy.

3 oz smoked salmon (or lox)	2 large tomatoes, preferably heirloom
3 eggs	2 scallions, thinly sliced (white part
Splash of water	and tips of green part)
1 Tbs heavy (whipping) cream	1 Tbs butter or olive oil
Salt and white pepper to taste	1 Tbs chives, divided

Procedure

1. Preheat the oven to 375° and line a small sheet pan with foil. Spray foil with cooking spray.
2. Cut the salmon (or lox) into small pieces.
3. In a small bowl beat the eggs, water and cream. Season with salt and white pepper.
4. Cut the top 1/3 of the tomatoes off and discard. Using a small paring knife (or grapefruit spoon) cut around the inside of the tomato being careful not to puncture the bottom or sides. Using a small spoon, scoop out the flesh along with the seeds. Chop the flesh and drain in a strainer to remove as much of the liquid as possible and set aside. Dab the inside of the tomato cups with paper towels to remove excess liquid. Place on prepared baking sheet and bake for 4 - 5 minutes until soft.
5. In a small non-stick skillet melt the butter or olive oil over medium-low heat and cook scallions 3 – 4 minutes until tender. Pour in the eggs and cook stirring constantly for 1 minute. Add the smoked salmon, reserved tomato pieces, and most of the snipped chives, reserving a bit for garnish. Continue to cook, stirring for another few minutes until the eggs reach desired firmness.
6. Place tomatoes on serving plates (use paper towels to mop up any extra liquid). Spoon scrambled eggs into tomato cups, garnish with reserved chives and serve.

Servings: 2

Preparation Time: 10 minutes
Cooking Time: 10 minutes

Nutrition Facts

Serving size: 1 tomato cup

Cook's Notes

Amount Per Serving	
Calories	168.94
Calories From Fat (33%)	55.32
	% Daily Value
Total Fat 6.35g	10%
Saturated Fat 1.05g	5%
Cholesterol 9.78mg	3%
Sodium 1376.14mg	57%
Potassium 659.85mg	19%
Total Carbohydrates 16.6g	6%
Fiber 3.42g	14%
Sugar 3.46g	
Protein 13.94g	28%

Tomato & Cheese Strata ⅔

Try using a different type of cheese. For example use blue cheese crumbles or shredded Parmesan, smoked Gouda or cheddar. You can also combine different fresh herbs such as tarragon, marjoram, parsley, dill or basil.

2	large	eggs
1/4	cup	plain Greek-style yogurt
2	Tbs	chopped fresh parsley
1	Tbs	olive oil
1/2		medium sweet onion, thinly sliced

1	Tbs	chopped fresh thyme leaves
1/2	tsp	smoked paprika (optional)
1 (14.5 oz)		can diced tomatoes with liquid
Salt and pepper to taste		
2	cups	1-inch cubed whole grain bread
2	Tbs	crumbled feta cheese

Procedure

1. Preheat oven to 450°.
2. In a medium bowl whisk together eggs, yogurt and parsley. Set aside.
3. In a medium size oven proof skillet (about 8"), heat olive oil over medium heat. Add onion and sauté over moderate heat until onions are soft and lightly brown, about 3 minutes. Add thyme and smoked paprika (if using) and stir to combine.
4. Add tomatoes with liquid, season with salt and pepper to taste, and bring to a simmer. Stir in bread cubes, remove from the heat, and sprinkle in the feta.
5. Pour egg mixture over top and bake for 20 - 25 minutes until golden brown. Allow to cool for a few minutes before serving in wedges.

Servings: 4

Preparation Time: 30 minutes
Cooking Time: 20 minutes

Nutrition Facts

Serving size: 1 wedge

Cook's Notes

Amount Per Serving	
Calories	327.97
Calories From Fat (61%)	199.93
	% Daily Value
Total Fat 22.64g	35%
Saturated Fat 12.77g	64%
Cholesterol 160.67mg	54%
Sodium 957.77mg	40%
Potassium 310.29mg	9%
Total Carbohydrates 14.75g	5%
Fiber 2.35g	9%
Sugar 7.09g	
Protein 17.23g	34%

C repes are a lovely vehicle for stuffing and fillings whether used for dessert or a quick sandwich. Add some leftover vegetables, a little cheese and voilà, you're done!

The popovers (or Yorkshire pudding) are tasty with a bit of gravy added. No one made them like my adopted English nana, Rose Lovett.

Crepes (page 38)

Popovers (page 39)

Crepes

These lovelies can be served as a dessert by spreading them with Nutella or a fruit jam. You can make them savory by using egg salad and sprinkling on a little fresh dill. They are very versatile.

2	large	eggs	1/2	cup	milk or unsweetened almond milk
1/2	cup	all-purpose flour			
1/4	tsp	salt	2	Tbs	carbonated water

Procedure

1 Place all ingredients, except carbonated water, in a blender and process into a smooth, thin batter. Let it rest in the refrigerator for at least 30 minutes. Stir in carbonated water just before cooking.

2 Heat a small 8" skillet or crepe pan and brush lightly with butter. Using a small ladle (2 - 3 tablespoons) pour batter into pan swirling to coat evenly. Cook until bubbles form on top and edges start to curl, about 2 minutes turn crepe over and cook on second side about 30 seconds. Transfer to a plate and cover with a large lid to fit over plate to keep warm. Repeat with remaining batter until used up.

Servings: 4
Yield: 8 - 10 crepes

Preparation Time: 5 minutes
Cooking Time: 15 minutes
Inactive Time: 30 minutes

Nutrition Facts

Serving size: 2 or 3 crepes

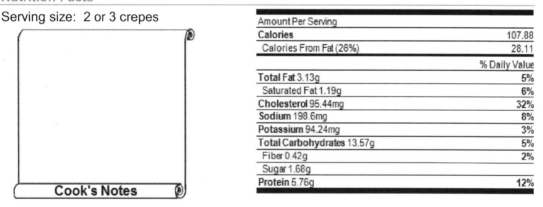

Cook's Notes

Amount Per Serving	
Calories	107.88
Calories From Fat (26%)	28.11
	% Daily Value
Total Fat 3.13g	5%
Saturated Fat 1.19g	6%
Cholesterol 95.44mg	32%
Sodium 198.6mg	8%
Potassium 94.24mg	3%
Total Carbohydrates 13.57g	5%
Fiber 0.42g	2%
Sugar 1.68g	
Protein 5.76g	12%

Recipe Tips

The first crepe is usually a mess, toss it away and continue. Use sheets of wax paper between crepes to keep from sticking.

Popovers (Yorkshire Pudding) ½

Sometimes I use leftover duck fat instead of butter; traditionally beef dripping is used.

3	large	eggs, lightly beaten	1/2	tsp	salt
1	cup	milk	2	Tbs	melted butter or oil
3/4	cup	unbleached all-purpose flour	1	Tbs	club soda or Perrier

Procedure

1. Preheat oven to 425°. Brush an 8 cup muffin tin generously with butter. Set aside.
2. In a medium-size bowl, whisk together eggs, milk, flour, salt, and remaining butter. Set aside to rest 10 - 15 minutes.
3. Place muffin tin into oven for 2 minutes to preheat.
4. Meanwhile, whisk club soda into batter, ladle into the pre-warmed muffin tins only until half full. Bake until puffed and golden, about 30 minutes.

Servings: 8

Preparation Time: 10 minutes
Cooking Time: 30 minutes

Nutrition Facts

Serving size: 1 popover

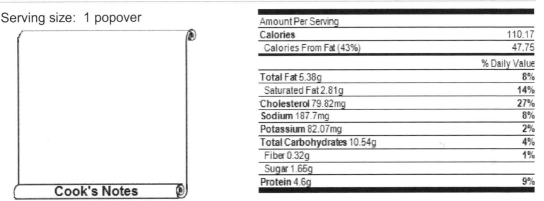

Cook's Notes

Amount Per Serving	
Calories	110.17
Calories From Fat (43%)	47.75
	% Daily Value
Total Fat 5.38g	8%
Saturated Fat 2.81g	14%
Cholesterol 79.82mg	27%
Sodium 187.7mg	8%
Potassium 82.07mg	2%
Total Carbohydrates 10.54g	4%
Fiber 0.32g	1%
Sugar 1.65g	
Protein 4.6g	9%

Recipe Tips

Don't peek! Popovers rise because of the steam created by the heat of the oven. If you open the oven door, the steam escapes causing them to fall.

M y husband has always had a sweet tooth. One of his favorite flavors was chocolate and it took many months for him to be able to taste it again. It still remains an elusive flavor for him on low saliva days but   one of his favorite chocolate puddings is made from avocados and cocoa powder. The avocado adds smoothness and great nutrients such as, potassium, Vitamins E, B and fiber, while the cocoa powder provides great chocolate flavor.

Nutella Chocolate Pudding (page 53)

Raspberry Fool (page 56)

Floating Island (page 50)

Cherry Clafouti (page 46)

40

This is a version of Annemarie Colbin's recipe from The Natural Gourmet cookbook. Her school is now called The Natural Gourmet Institute and is located in Manhattan.

2 1/2	cup	almond milk (organic, unsweetened), divided	1/2	tsp	almond extract
			1	Tbs	vanilla extract
2 (1/4 oz)	packets	unflavored gelatin	6	oz	raspberry jam (seedless)
2	Tbs	corn starch (or arrowroot)	6	Tbs	water
1/4	cup	maple syrup			

Procedure

1 In a saucepan add 2 cups of the almond milk and sprinkle gelatin on top. Gently simmer over low heat until completely dissolved.

2 In a small bowl combine the cornstarch with the remaining 1/2 cup of almond milk, stir in the maple syrup and the extracts and add to the saucepan. Stir continuously over high heat until mixture comes to a boil and thickens.

3 Rinse serving bowls or ramekins with cold water, divide mixture evenly and chill until firm, about 2 hours.

4 Mix together the raspberry jam and water to make the sauce. Warm the sauce just before serving.

5 To serve, run a knife along the edges of the flan and invert onto serving plates. Spoon sauce over top and serve.

Servings: 4

Preparation Time: 10 minutes
Cooking Time: 5 minutes
Inactive Time: 2 hours

Nutrition Facts

Serving size: 1 flan

Cook's Notes

Amount Per Serving	
Calories	165.67
Calories From Fat (12%)	20.19
	% Daily Value
Total Fat 1.97g	3%
Saturated Fat 0g	0%
Cholesterol 0mg	0%
Sodium 130.98mg	5%
Potassium 157mg	4%
Total Carbohydrates 35.93g	12%
Fiber 1.23g	5%
Sugar 3.77g	
Protein 0.5g	1%

Almond - Vanilla Panna Cotta

This was featured on one of Sandra Lee's cooking programs and is super creamy. I sometimes use agave nectar instead of the sugar.

1	cup	unsweetened almond milk, divided	3/4	tsp	almond extract
1 (1/4 oz)		packet unflavored gelatin	1	tsp	vanilla extract
1 1/2	cups	heavy (whipping) cream	1/4	cup	chocolate syrup
1/2	cup	sugar	Sliced strawberries for serving (optional)		

Procedure

1 Pour 1/3 cup almond milk into a small bowl and stir in gelatin Set aside.

2 In a medium saucepan, stir together heavy cream, remaining almond milk, and sugar. Bring to boil over medium heat, stirring often.

3 Pour gelatin mixture into cream mixture and stir until gelatin completely dissolves. Add 1/2 teaspoon almond extract and the vanilla extract and cook for 1 minute, stirring constantly. Remove from heat and pour into 6 dessert cups or martini glasses.

4 When cooled to room temperature cover with plastic wrap and refrigerate for at least 4 hours (or overnight).

5 In a glass measuring cup, stir 1/4 cup chocolate syrup with 1/4 teaspoon almond extract. Drizzle over the top of the panna cottas and serve. Place a sliced strawberry on top for a treat.

Servings: 6

Preparation Time: 10 minutes
Cooking Time: 10 minutes
Inactive Time: 4 hours

Nutrition Facts

Serving size: ½ cup

Cook's Notes

Amount Per Serving	
Calories	226.26
Calories From Fat (48%)	108.45
	% Daily Value
Total Fat 12.27g	19%
Saturated Fat 7.46g	37%
Cholesterol 41.06mg	14%
Sodium 99.73mg	4%
Potassium 159.94mg	5%
Total Carbohydrates 27.04g	9%
Fiber 0.79g	3%
Sugar 22.21g	
Protein 2.49g	5%

Apple Custard Pie

This is from the Moosewood Cookbook which was my constant companion when my husband and I were vegetarians in the mid 1980's. This is not your typical apple pie – it's much smoother.

1 9"	whole wheat pie shell, unbaked	1/4	cup	agave syrup
2 large	apples, peeled, cored and finely-grated	1/2	cup	maple syrup
1 Tbs	almond meal	1	tsp	vanilla extract
1 cup	plain Greek-style yogurt	1/2	tsp	pumpkin pie spice mix, or cinnamon
4 large	eggs	1/4	tsp salt	

Procedure

1. Preheat oven to 375°.
2. Combine apples with the almond meal and place in bottom of pie shell.
3. Combine all other ingredients in a blender and puree at high speed until well combined.
4. Pour mixture over the apples and bake 45 minutes until center does not jiggle when shaken.

Servings: 8
Yield: 1-9" Pie

Preparation Time: 15 minutes
Cooking Time: 45 minutes

Nutrition Facts

Serving size: 1/8 of pie

Cook's Notes

Amount Per Serving	
Calories	136.57
Calories From Fat (23%)	31.13
	% Daily Value
Total Fat 3.47g	5%
Saturated Fat 1.26g	6%
Cholesterol 94.73mg	32%
Sodium 139.76mg	6%
Potassium 171.01mg	5%
Total Carbohydrates 21.8g	7%
Fiber 0.43g	2%
Sugar 16.52g	
Protein 4.86g	10%

Ariel Gelatin Parfait

Ariel is a non-alcoholic sparkling wine. It is normally less expensive than even a cheap bottle of alcoholic sparkling wine and has no compromise in flavor. Thank you Claire Robinson for this great idea!

1	bottle	Ariel Brut Cuvée Sparkling Wine	2 (1/4 oz)		packets unflavored gelatin
3/4	cup	sugar, divided	1 cup		heavy (whipping) cream
1/2	cup	water	1 cup		mascarpone cheese

Procedure

1 Pour entire bottle of Ariel, 1/2 cup of sugar and water into a large sauce pan. Bring to a boil over high heat, reduce heat to low and simmer for 5 minutes. Remove from heat and whisk in the gelatin until completely dissolved.

2 Pour into a 9 x 11 inch glass baking dish, cool to room temperature and chill for 4 hours in the refrigerator.

3 In a large bowl whip the cream to medium stiff peaks.

4 In another bowl mix the mascarpone with the remaining 1/4 cup of sugar. Mix in 1/3 of the mascarpone to the whipped cream to lighten, then carefully fold in the remaining whipped cream.

5 Cut the gelatin into 1 x 1 inch squares and put a layer in the bottom of each parfait glass, spoon a layer of mascarpone mixture on top of gelatin and repeat layers.

Servings: 8

Nutrition Facts

Serving size: 1 parfait

Cook's Notes

Amount Per Serving	
Calories	425.59
Calories From Fat (37%)	155.35
	% Daily Value
Total Fat 17.54g	27%
Saturated Fat 6.86g	34%
Cholesterol 60.2mg	20%
Sodium 224.45mg	9%
Potassium 2416.46mg	69%
Total Carbohydrates 50.08g	17%
Fiber 0g	0%
Sugar 48.65g	
Protein 20.94g	42%

Use nut milk, whole milk, or low-fat milk. The frozen bananas make a ton of noise while processing, but hang in there, it's worth it. It tastes just like ice cream - really!

2	very ripe	bananas, peeled and sliced	1/4	tsp	vanilla extract
1/4	cup	coconut milk			

Procedure

1 Freeze bananas.

2 Place in a small food processor and process until well crumbled.

3 Add coconut milk and vanilla and process until smooth, scraping down the bowl as necessary.

Servings: 2

Preparation Time: 10 minutes
Cooking Time:
Inactive Time: 6 hours

Nutrition Facts

Serving size: about 1/2 cup

Cook's Notes

Amount Per Serving	
Calories	167.13
Calories From Fat (33%)	55.4
	% Daily Value
Total Fat 6.63g	10%
Saturated Fat 5.67g	28%
Cholesterol 0mg	0%
Sodium 4.83mg	<1%
Potassium 492.82mg	14%
Total Carbohydrates 28.69g	10%
Fiber 3.07g	12%
Sugar 14.5g	
Protein 1.77g	4%

Cherry Clafouti ¼

My friend Nancy Bodenheimer made this for us using fresh cherries. This is my quick rendition using a blender and frozen cherries.

1	cup	frozen cherries, thawed
1/4	cup	heavy (whipping) cream
1/4	cup	almond milk (organic, unsweetened)
1/4	cup	maple syrup (or agave nectar)
1/2	cup	cottage cheese
2	large	eggs

1/4	cup	quinoa flour, (or unbleached white flour)
1/4	cup	almond meal
1/4	tsp	cinnamon
1	tsp	vanilla extract
1/4	tsp	almond extract, (optional)
		Powdered sugar for garnish

Procedure

1 Preheat oven to 375°.

2 Put all ingredients, except cherries into a blender, and puree until smooth, 1 - 2 minutes.

3 Pour into an 8" round oven safe dish (or pie plate) which has been lightly coated with cooking spray. Arrange cherries over the top and bake for 35 - 40 minutes or until puffed and brown. Allow to cool to room temperature before sprinkling with powdered sugar.

4 Cut into wedges or scoop onto dessert plates.

Servings: 8

Preparation Time: 15 minutes
Cooking Time: 40 minutes

Nutrition Facts

Serving size: 1/8 of pie

Cook's Notes

Amount Per Serving	
Calories	96.83
Calories From Fat (42%)	40.26

	% Daily Value
Total Fat 4.53g	7%
Saturated Fat 2.26g	11%
Cholesterol 58.1mg	19%
Sodium 74.49mg	3%
Potassium 86.65mg	2%
Total Carbohydrates 10.31g	3%
Fiber 0.45g	2%
Sugar 8.34g	
Protein 3.71g	7%

These are the most decadent truffles. I make a big batch for the holidays and give them as gifts. The secret is the addition of the cranberry sauce.

2	cups	chopped dark chocolate (about 12 oz.)
1	cup	heavy (whipping) cream
1/2	cup	whole berry cranberry sauce
		Zest of half an orange
1/4	cup	unsalted butter , softened

1/4	cup	finely chopped nuts, candy sprinkles, coconut, or cocoa powder (optional)

Procedure

1 Place chopped chocolate in a medium size glass bowl.

2 In a small saucepan over medium high heat, warm cream until small bubbles form on side of pan. Do not allow to boil. Pour over chocolate, gently stirring until chocolate melts. Add cranberry sauce, orange zest, and butter and whisk until incorporated. Press cling wrap directly on top of mixture, chill for 4 hours or overnight in refrigerator.

3 Wearing rubber gloves and using a small scoop, or spoon, roll chocolate into balls. Place on a parchment-lined sheet tray (or use a silpat mat). Roll chocolate balls in nuts, sprinkles, coconut, or cocoa powder if desired. Chill for about 15 minutes before serving.

Servings: 35
Yield: 35 truffles

Preparation Time: 10 minutes
Cooking Time: 15 minutes
Inactive Time: 4 hours

Nutrition Facts

Serving size: 1 truffle

Cook's Notes

Amount Per Serving	
Calories	80.7
Calories From Fat (75%)	60.35
	% Daily Value
Total Fat 6.83g	11%
Saturated Fat 3.85g	19%
Cholesterol 12.97mg	4%
Sodium 5.06mg	<1%
Potassium 50.75mg	1%
Total Carbohydrates 4.48g	1%
Fiber 0.75g	3%
Sugar 2.91g	
Protein 0.68g	1%

Chocolate Mousse Surprise

Talk about smooth! The surprise is the avocado which can be kept a secret. No one will guess what it's actually made of.

2		avocados, preferably Hass	1/2	tsp	cinnamon
6	oz	vanilla yogurt	1/2	tsp	instant coffee granules (optional)
1/2	cup	agave nectar (or honey)	1	pinch	salt
1/2	cup	unsweetened cocoa powder	2	large	egg whites
1	tsp	vanilla extract	1/4	cup	powdered sugar
1/2	tsp	almond extract	Shaved chocolate for garnish		

Procedure

1 Cut avocado in half, discard the seed and scoop flesh into a food processor fitted with a metal blade.

2 Add next 8 ingredients and process until completely smooth, scrapping down the sides if necessary. Transfer mixture into a large mixing bowl.

3 In a small bowl, whip egg whites until frothy, adding powdered sugar in stages and whipping to stiff peaks.

4 Add a small amount of whipped egg whites to avocado mixture to lighten. Gently fold in remaining and egg whites in stages, folding until almost incorporated (a few white streaks are fine).

5 Divide into serving bowls (or wine glasses) and chill before serving. Top with shaved chocolate or tiny chocolate chips.

Servings: 6

Preparation Time: 5 minutes
Inactive Time: 2 hours

Nutrition Facts

Serving size: about 1/2 cup

Amount Per Serving	
Calories	188.44
Calories From Fat (44%)	83.73
	% Daily Value
Total Fat 9.92g	15%
Saturated Fat 1.87g	9%
Cholesterol 3.77mg	1%
Sodium 460.39mg	19%
Potassium 486.85mg	14%
Total Carbohydrates 20.83g	7%
Fiber 4.19g	17%
Sugar 15.56g	
Protein 6.15g	12%

This is an adaptation of Giada De Laurentiis' creation. It's smooth and rich.

1/2	cup	almond milk (organic, unsweetened)	3	tsp	instant espresso powder
1 1/2	tsp	unflavored gelatin	1/4	cup	sugar or equivalent sweetener
1 1/2	cups	heavy (whipping) cream			Pinch of salt
					Grated dark chocolate for garnish

Procedure

1. In a small saucepan pour almond milk, sprinkle gelatin on top and let stand 5 minutes to soften gelatin. Stir over medium heat until gelatin dissolves, about 2 minutes (do not boil).
2. Add cream, espresso powder, sugar and salt. Stir over low heat until everything dissolves, about 5 more minutes.
3. Pour mixture into 2 martini glasses, cover and refrigerate, stirring every 20 minutes during first hour. Chill until set, 4 hours (or overnight).
4. Garnish with grated dark chocolate or tiny chocolate chips just before serving.

Servings: 2

Preparation Time: 5 minutes
Cooking Time: 15 minutes
Inactive Time: 4 hours

Nutrition Facts

Serving size: about 1 cup

Cook's Notes

Amount Per Serving	
Calories	743.42
Calories From Fat (79%)	588.73
	% Daily Value
Total Fat 66.81g	103%
Saturated Fat 41.12g	206%
Cholesterol 244.55mg	82%
Sodium 269.21mg	11%
Potassium 230.47mg	7%
Total Carbohydrates 31.03g	10%
Fiber 0.25g	1%
Sugar 25.15g	
Protein 8.32g	17%

This dessert originated in France as "Oeufs à la Neige" or "Floating Island" consisting of large meringue puffs floating on vanilla custard. Honey or maple syrup may also be used instead of the agave syrup. It's a favorite in Hungary - literally translating to Bird's Milk.

2 1/2	cups	almond milk (organic, unsweetened)
1/4	cup	agave syrup
4		large eggs, separated
Pinch of salt		

1/4	tsp	cream of tartar
1/4	cup	sugar or equivalent sweetener, divided
1	tsp	vanilla extract
Cinnamon or cocoa powder for serving		

Procedure

1 Heat almond milk and the agave syrup until bubbles form on the side of the pan.

2 Meanwhile, beat egg whites with a pinch of salt until frothy. Add the cream of tartar, gradually increase speed and add 2 tablespoons of the sugar, beating until stiff peaks form.

3 Drop large dollops of the stiffened egg whites into the simmering almond milk using a large spoon. After 1 minute turn them over to cook 1 more minute. Remove; setting the "islands" on paper towels to drain.

4 Combine egg yolks and remainder of 2 tablespoons of sugar and beat until pale yellow in color. Temper the yolks by adding tiny amounts of the hot almond milk while whisking being careful not to curdle the yolk mixture. Pour this tempered mixture back into the simmering pot of almond milk and stir gently to thicken slightly. Remove from the heat and stir in vanilla extract, cool to room temperature.

5 Pour into dessert bowls, scoop the white "islands" on top and chill completely.

6 To serve, sprinkle with cinnamon or cocoa powder.

Servings: 4

Preparation Time: 20 minutes
Inactive Time: 2 hours

Nutrition Facts

Serving size: about ¾ cup

Cook's Notes

Amount Per Serving	
Calories	152.41
Calories From Fat (37%)	56.98
	% Daily Value
Total Fat 6.06g	9%
Saturated Fat 1.38g	7%
Cholesterol 163.68mg	55%
Sodium 247.97mg	10%
Potassium 212.23mg	6%
Total Carbohydrates 17.67g	6%
Fiber 0.63g	3%
Sugar 16.13g	
Protein 5.53g	11%

Kahlúamisu ½₂

This is a quick Tiramisu-type dessert that is fabulous and goes down so easily.

1/2	cup	brewed espresso coffee, cooled			Pinch of salt
1	Tbs	Kahlúa liqueur	1/4	cup	palm sugar, (or brown sugar)
6	soft	lady fingers	1	Tbs	cocoa powder or grated chocolate for garnish
2/3	cup	heavy (whipping) cream			

Procedure

1 In a small shallow dish, mix espresso with Kahlúa and set aside.

2 In another small bowl, whip cream with the salt and sugar into soft peaks.

3 Split lady fingers into 12 halves. Working quickly, dip 6 halves into espresso-Kahlúa mixture and place into martini glasses as first layer (the ends will extend beyond the glass). Spoon a dollop of whipped cream in the center, make another layer with remaining lady fingers and whipped cream. Sprinkle with cocoa powder or grated chocolate and serve or refrigerate until serving.

Servings: 2

Preparation Time: 5 minutes

Nutrition Facts

Serving size: about 3/4 cup

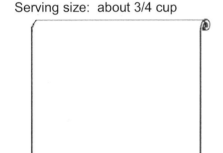

Cook's Notes

Amount Per Serving	
Calories	510.46
Calories From Fat (58%)	295.8
	% Daily Value
Total Fat 33.55g	52%
Saturated Fat 19.98g	100%
Cholesterol 194.88mg	65%
Sodium 251.89mg	10%
Potassium 282.99mg	8%
Total Carbohydrates 39.51g	13%
Fiber 1.29g	5%
Sugar 12.43g	
Protein 6.45g	13%

No-Cook Brownies

Adapted from Ulli Stachel via the Dr. Oz Show, these are tasty little treats.

1	cup	unsweetened cocoa powder	1 cup raisins (or dried cranberries)
2	tsp	cinnamon	1 cup quinoa flakes (or rolled oats)
1/2	cup	almond milk (organic, unsweetened)	

Procedure

1 In a food processor purée cocoa powder, cinnamon, almond milk and raisins (or cranberries) until smooth, 1 - 2 minutes.

2 Add quinoa flakes (or oats) and pulse several times to incorporate.

3 Transfer mixture into a 5 ½" square container which has been sprayed with cooking spray. Press down and even out mixture with a rubber spatula. Refrigerate until firm and cut into small squares.

Servings: 12
Yield: 12 small squares

Preparation Time: 10 minutes

Nutrition Facts

Serving size: 1 square

Cook's Notes

Amount Per Serving	
Calories	72.18
Calories From Fat (17%)	12.09
	% Daily Value
Total Fat 1.42g	2%
Saturated Fat 0.23g	1%
Cholesterol 0mg	0%
Sodium 13.52mg	<1%
Potassium 249.28mg	7%
Total Carbohydrates 16.47g	5%
Fiber 3.72g	15%
Sugar 8.39g	
Protein 1.59g	3%

Nutella® Chocolate Pudding

This spread was created in the 1940s by Pietro Ferrero, a pastry maker. There was very little chocolate because cocoa was in short supply during World War II rationing. It is a combination of roasted hazelnuts, skim milk and a hint of cocoa. It has no artificial colors or preservatives.

1/2	cup	chocolate hazelnut spread (Nutella®)	1/2	cup	heavy (whipping) cream
			Pinch of salt		
1/4	cup	vanilla yogurt	1 1/2	tsp	hazelnut liqueur (optional)

Procedure

1 In a medium bowl, using an electric mixer on low speed beat the Nutella and yogurt until smooth and creamy. Set aside.

2 In a small bowl, beat the cream with a pinch of salt to firm peaks adding liqueur toward the end if using.

3 Using a rubber spatula, take some of the whipped cream and stir into Nutella yogurt mixture to lighten. Fold in remaining whipped cream carefully until all the whipped cream is incorporated.

4 Spoon mousse into dessert bowls and refrigerate for about 20 minutes before serving.

Servings: 4

Preparation Time: 10 minutes
Inactive Time: 30 minutes

Nutrition Facts

Serving size: about 1/3 cup

Cook's Notes

Amount Per Serving	
Calories	147.55
Calories From Fat (75%)	110.94

	% Daily Value
Total Fat 12.57g	19%
Saturated Fat 8.29g	41%
Cholesterol 41.52mg	14%
Sodium 23.31mg	<1%
Potassium 74.67mg	2%
Total Carbohydrates 6.51g	2%
Fiber 0.25g	1%
Sugar 4.65g	
Protein 1.61g	3%

Recipe Tips

Use 1 tsp almond or hazelnut extract in place of the liqueur.

Peach Fool

This is such an easy dessert. A terrific alternative uses frozen mango pieces which echo the flavor of the mango-peach yogurt.

10	ounces	frozen sliced peaches, thawed	1/4	cup	whipping cream
1 1/2	cups	mango-peach yogurt	Pinch of salt		
1/4	cup	sugar or equivalent sweetener			

Procedure

1. Place peaches in a food processor, add sugar, and process until sugar is dissolved and mixture is smooth.
2. Add yogurt and pulse to combine. Remove to a medium-size bowl and set aside.
3. In a small bowl, whip cream with a pinch of salt into soft peaks.
4. Gently fold whipped cream into peach mixture.
5. Pour into 4 dessert bowls and chill for at least 2 hours before serving.

Servings: 4

Preparation Time: 25 minutes
Cooking Time: 10 minutes

Nutrition Facts

Serving size: about ½ cup

Cook's Notes

Amount Per Serving	
Calories	166.72
Calories From Fat (37%)	62.27
	% Daily Value
Total Fat 7.11g	11%
Saturated Fat 4.18g	21%
Cholesterol 24.97mg	8%
Sodium 67.27mg	3%
Potassium 319.38mg	9%
Total Carbohydrates 21.68g	7%
Fiber 4.61g	18%
Sugar 15.92g	
Protein 5.68g	11%

Pumpkin Pudding

I love the flavor of pumpkin in the fall. Serve it slightly warm.

3	cups	unsweetened pumpkin puree	1	tsp	pumpkin pie spice
3/4	cup	maple syrup	1/2	tsp	ground ginger
2	Tbs	molasses	1	tsp	salt
1/4	tsp	ground cloves	4 large		eggs, lightly beaten
2	tsp	cinnamon	2	cups	almond milk (organic, unsweetened)

Procedure

1. Put pumpkin purée into a large mixing bowl and add remaining ingredients as listed until incorporated.
2. Pour mixture into a 1 quart buttered baking dish and bake 40 minutes or until set.

Servings: 8

Preparation Time: 15 minutes
Cooking Time: 40 minutes

Nutrition Facts

Serving size: about 1 cup

Cook's Notes

Amount Per Serving	
Calories	171.19
Calories From Fat (19%)	31.92
	% Daily Value
Total Fat 3.46g	5%
Saturated Fat 0.94g	5%
Cholesterol 93mg	31%
Sodium 381.54mg	16%
Potassium 413.55mg	12%
Total Carbohydrates 32.44g	11%
Fiber 3.33g	13%
Sugar 23.78g	
Protein 4.21g	8%

Raspberry Fool

I wish raspberries didn't have such large seeds! This comes from Ellie Krieger.

10	ounces	frozen raspberries, thawed	1 1/2	cups	vanilla yogurt
1/3	cup	sugar or equivalent sweetener	1/4	cup	whipping cream
			Pinch of salt		

Procedure

1. Place raspberries in a food processor, add sugar and process until sugar is dissolved.
2. Scrape into a strainer placed over a bowl and stir until liquid is extracted, leaving behind the seeds. Discard the seeds.
3. Fold yogurt into strained raspberry sauce.
4. In a small bowl, whip the cream with a pinch of salt until soft peaks form.
5. Gently fold whipped cream into raspberry mixture.
6. Pour into 4 champagne glasses and chill for at least 2 hours before serving.

Servings: 4

Preparation Time: 25 minutes
Cooking Time: 10 minutes

Nutrition Facts

Serving size: 1/2 cup

Cook's Notes

Amount Per Serving	
Calories	174.03
Calories From Fat (45%)	78.62
	% Daily Value
Total Fat 8.99g	14%
Saturated Fat 5.29g	26%
Cholesterol 21.46mg	7%
Sodium 53.34mg	2%
Potassium 232.12mg	7%
Total Carbohydrates 22.02g	7%
Fiber 4.61g	18%
Sugar 16.11g	
Protein 3.32g	7%

56

Try using small-curd cottage cheese if ricotta is too dry to swallow.

8 oz	ricotta cheese	1	tsp	orange peel, freshly grated
2 packets	Stevia, French vanilla flavor	1	tsp	lime peel, freshly grated
1 tsp	lemon peel, freshly grated	1/4	tsp	vanilla extract

Procedure

1 In a medium-size bowl mix everything together until well combined. Divide mixture into decorative serving bowls, and enjoy.

Servings: 2

Preparation Time: 5 minutes
Cooking Time:

Nutrition Facts

Serving size: ½ cup

Cook's Notes

Amount Per Serving	
Calories	217.62
Calories From Fat (64%)	138.65
	% Daily Value
Total Fat 15.97g	25%
Saturated Fat 10.2g	51%
Cholesterol 62.73mg	21%
Sodium 103.52mg	4%
Potassium 135.25mg	4%
Total Carbohydrates 5.08g	2%
Fiber 0.32g	1%
Sugar 0.44g	
Protein 13.9g	28%

This is a lovely winter dessert. The quinoa flakes makes the topping much easier to swallow.

1/2	cup	palm sugar (or light brown sugar)	2		Bosc pears, peeled, cored, and sliced
1/4		cup quinoa flour	1/3	cup	dried cranberries, currants or raisins
2 Tbs		pecans			
1 tsp		ground cinnamon	2	Tbs	palm sugar (or light brown sugar)
1/2	stick	unsalted butter cut into small pieces	1	tsp	ground cinnamon
1/2	cup	quinoa flakes (or rolled oats)	1/8	tsp	ground cardamom
2		Granny Smith apples, peeled, cored, and thinly sliced	2	Tbs	maple syrup

Procedure

1 Preheat oven to 350°.Butter a 12-inch cast-iron skillet, oven-proof skillet or large deep dish pie plate.

Make the topping

2 In a food processor combine sugar with flour, pecans and cinnamon. Add butter and pulse until the mixture is grainy. Transfer topping to a bowl and press into clumps.

Make the filling

3 In a large bowl combine apples, pears, dried cranberries (currants, or raisins), palm sugar, cinnamon, cardamom, and agave and stir until the sugar is incorporated.

4 Spread the fruit on bottom of the skillet and scatter the clumps of topping over the fruit.

5 Bake the crisp in the center of the oven for 45 minutes to 1 hour, until the fruit is bubbling and topping is brown. Let cool for 10 minutes before serving.

Servings: 8
Preparation Time: 20 minutes
Cooking Time: 1 hour

Nutrition Facts

Serving size: ½ cup

Cook's Notes

Amount Per Serving	
Calories	236.19
Calories From Fat (30%)	71.41
	% Daily Value
Total Fat 8.24g	13%
Saturated Fat 3.92g	20%
Cholesterol 15.18mg	5%
Sodium 6.32mg	<1%
Potassium 370.84mg	11%
Total Carbohydrates 43.87g	15%
Fiber 8.1g	32%
Sugar 25.93g	
Protein 2.28g	5%

Recipe Tips

This is wonderful served with vanilla ice cream.

make between four to five smoothies per day. Basically I combine fruits with nut milk, add a bit of sweetener and flavored flax oil such as lemon, cinnamon, or pomegranate and blend. Avocado is wonderful as a good base ingredient because it doesn't have a strong flavor of its own and it's very smooth. It's hard to make a mistake by just combining a few ingredients. Use the recipes as a guide and use your own creativity.

Cherry Smoothie (page 65)

Almond Butter - Banana Smoothie (page 61)

Blueberry Smoothie (page 64)

Avocado - Almond Milk Smoothie (page 62)

"Green" Banana Smoothie

The frozen banana removes any taste of the spinach but the smoothie is still a green color.

1 cup	baby spinach (about a handful)	1 small	banana, peeled. mashed & frozen
1 cup	coconut milk or other nut milk	1 Tbs	honey

Procedure

1 Place all ingredients into a small blender and process until completely smooth.

Servings: 1

Preparation Time: 5 minutes

Nutrition Facts

Cook's Notes

Amount Per Serving	
Calories	216.47
Calories From Fat (4%)	8.05
	% Daily Value
Total Fat 0.97g	1%
Saturated Fat 0.57g	3%
Cholesterol 0mg	0%
Sodium 277.67mg	12%
Potassium 1181.07mg	34%
Total Carbohydrates 52.99g	18%
Fiber 6.27g	25%
Sugar 37.39g	
Protein 3.88g	8%

Almond butter has a sweeter flavor than peanut butter, but any nut butter can be used.

1/2	cup	almond milk (organic, unsweetened)
1/2	cup	plain yogurt
1	Tbs	flax oil, cinnamon flavored
3	Tbs	almond butter
1	small	banana, peeled and sliced
1/4	tsp	cinnamon
2	Tbs	unsweetened cocoa powder

Procedure

1 Put all ingredients into a blender and purée until smooth.

Servings: 2
Yield: 2 cups

Preparation Time: 5 minutes

Nutrition Facts

Serving size: 1 cup

Cook's Notes

Amount Per Serving	
Calories	319.24
Calories From Fat (61%)	195.45
	% Daily Value
Total Fat 22.75g	35%
Saturated Fat 2.75g	14%
Cholesterol 3.68mg	1%
Sodium 141.2mg	6%
Potassium 655.42mg	19%
Total Carbohydrates 25.56g	9%
Fiber 6.15g	25%
Sugar 12.36g	
Protein 9.93g	20%

Avocado - Almond Milk Smoothie

I often use avocado as the base ingredient for a smoothie then add other fruits like berries or cherries.

1		avocado, preferably Hass
2	cups	almond milk (organic, unsweetened)
1/4	tsp	almond extract

2 Tbs		agave syrup
5 drops		stevia, vanilla flavored (optional)

Procedure

1 Cut avocado in half, discard seed, and scoop flesh into a blender.

2 Add remaining ingredients and process until smooth adding additional almond milk for desired consistency. Taste and add additional sweetener, if necessary.

Servings: 2

Preparation Time: 10 minutes

Nutrition Facts

Serving size: about 1 cup

Cook's Notes

Amount Per Serving	
Calories	197.84
Calories From Fat (72%)	143.23
	% Daily Value
Total Fat 16.34g	25%
Saturated Fat 1.84g	9%
Cholesterol 0mg	0%
Sodium 186.92mg	8%
Potassium 628.55mg	18%
Total Carbohydrates 12.83g	4%
Fiber 6.88g	28%
Sugar 3.62g	
Protein 1.7g	3%

Recipe Tips

To turn this into a chocolate smoothie, add 2 tablespoons of unsweetened cocoa powder

Banana Coconut Milk Smoothie

Bananas are great as a base ingredient for any smoothie.

1/2 medium banana, peeled and sliced	1 Tbs flax oil, cinnamon flavored
1 cup coconut milk	

Procedure

1 Place all ingredients into a small blender and process until completely smooth.

Servings: 1

Preparation Time: 5 minutes

Nutrition Facts

Cook's Notes

Amount Per Serving	
Calories	215.89
Calories From Fat (58%)	125.75
	% Daily Value
Total Fat 14.27g	22%
Saturated Fat 1.76g	9%
Cholesterol 0mg	0%
Sodium 252.56mg	11%
Potassium 801.38mg	23%
Total Carbohydrates 21.75g	7%
Fiber 4.1g	16%
Sugar 13.14g	
Protein 2.34g	5%

63

Blueberry Smoothie

Use a berry flavored herbal tea, like "Zinger"

1/2	cup	blueberries (fresh or frozen)	1/2	cup	plain yogurt, regular or low-fat
1	tsp	flax oil	1/4	cup	herbal tea

Procedure

1 Put all ingredients into a small blender and process until smooth.

Servings: 1

Nutrition Facts

Cook's Notes

Amount Per Serving	
Calories	159.23
Calories From Fat (37%)	58.74
	% Daily Value
Total Fat 6.68g	10%
Saturated Fat 1.67g	8%
Cholesterol 7.35mg	2%
Sodium 87.07mg	4%
Potassium 347.81mg	10%
Total Carbohydrates 19.25g	6%
Fiber 1.74g	7%
Sugar 15.85g	
Protein 6.97g	14%

Cherry Smoothie

To sweeten I like to add vanilla-flavored drops of Sweet Leaf® Stevia (5 - 6 drops or so).

2 cups	frozen cherries	1 cup	coconut water
1 ripe	banana, peeled and sliced	1 tsp	flax oil, cinnamon flavored

Procedure

1. Put frozen cherries, banana, coconut water and flax oil into a blender. Cover and process until completely smooth. Pour into individual serving glasses. Serve immediately.

Servings: 2

Nutrition Facts

Serving size: about 1 cup

Cook's Notes

Amount Per Serving	
Calories	166.68
Calories From Fat (18%)	29.34
	% Daily Value
Total Fat 3.39g	5%
Saturated Fat 0.65g	3%
Cholesterol 0mg	0%
Sodium 128.14mg	5%
Potassium 703.42mg	20%
Total Carbohydrates 35.01g	12%
Fiber 5.33g	21%
Sugar 24.33g	
Protein 2.93g	6%

Greens 'n Berries Smoothie

The psyllium is added to increase the fiber.

1/2	cup	baby spinach	1 cup	berries of choice (fresh or frozen)
1	cup	nut milk (organic, unsweetened)	1 Tbs	flax oil, cinnamon flavored (optional)
1	cup	green tea	2	psyllium capsule contents (optional)
1	small	banana, peeled. mashed & frozen		

Procedure

1 Place all ingredients in a blender adding the contents of the capsules last, if using. Blend on high speed until smooth.

Servings: 2

Preparation Time: 10 minutes

Nutrition Facts

Serving size: about 1 cup

Cook's Notes

Amount Per Serving	
Calories	174.11
Calories From Fat (46%)	79.33
	% Daily Value
Total Fat 8.75g	13%
Saturated Fat 0.73g	4%
Cholesterol 0mg	0%
Sodium 97.21mg	4%
Potassium 412.74mg	12%
Total Carbohydrates 24.89g	8%
Fiber 3.87g	15%
Sugar 14.13g	
Protein 1.36g	3%

Recipe Tips

If additional sweetness is needed, add a few drops of Sweet Leaf® Stevia or a touch of agave nectar or maple syrup.

Holiday Nog

This is yummy and can be served warmed up or cooled.

2	cups	almond milk (organic, unsweetened)	1	tsp	vanilla extract
1/3	cup	macadamia nuts	1	tsp	maple syrup (or agave syrup)
1	large	banana, peeled. mashed & frozen	1	tsp	flax oil, cinnamon flavored
3		dates, pitted (preferably Medjool)	1/4	tsp	pumpkin pie spice mix, or cinnamon

Ground nutmeg for serving

Procedure

1. Place all ingredients in blender and puree until very smooth.
2. Strain to remove any unwanted bits and serve with a sprinkle of nutmeg.

Servings: 2

Preparation Time: 5 minutes

Nutrition Facts

Serving size: 1 generous cup

Cook's Notes

Amount Per Serving	
Calories	312.1
Calories From Fat (58%)	180.17
	% Daily Value
Total Fat 21.05g	32%
Saturated Fat 3.06g	15%
Cholesterol 0mg	0%
Sodium 92.68mg	4%
Potassium 513.4mg	15%
Total Carbohydrates 31.6g	11%
Fiber 5.24g	21%
Sugar 19.59g	
Protein 2.83g	6%

Pumpkin Nog

This might taste even better slightly warmed, especially on cold winter nights.

1/2	cup	unsweetened pumpkin puree	1/2	tsp	pumpkin pie spice mix, or cinnamon
1 1/2	cups	coconut milk	1/4	tsp	vanilla extract
1		scoop ice cream (such as vanilla rum raisin)			Freshly ground nutmeg

Procedure

1 Put all ingredients in blender, except nutmeg, and process until smooth.

2 Pour into glasses or mugs, top with nutmeg and serve.

Servings: 2

Preparation Time: 5 minutes

Nutrition Facts

Serving size: about 1 cup

Cook's Notes

Amount Per Serving	
Calories	174.55
Calories From Fat (32%)	56.21
	% Daily Value
Total Fat 6.48g	10%
Saturated Fat 3.81g	19%
Cholesterol 12.76mg	4%
Sodium 224.14mg	9%
Potassium 660.35mg	19%
Total Carbohydrates 29.47g	10%
Fiber 5.59g	22%
Sugar 12.73g	
Protein 3.63g	7%

Yuletide Nog

Be sure to use raw cashews and not the roasted, salted variety.

2	cups	almond milk (organic, unsweetened)	1	tsp	vanilla extract
			1	tsp	flax oil, cinnamon flavored
1/3	cup	cashews	1	tsp	maple syrup
1	large	banana, peeled. mashed & frozen	1/4	tsp	ground nutmeg
3		dates, pitted and chopped			Ground cinnamon for serving

Procedure

1 Place all ingredients in a blender and purée until smooth.

2 Pour into glasses, sprinkle some cinnamon over the top and serve.

Servings: 4

Preparation Time: 10 minutes

Nutrition Facts

Serving size: about 1 cup

Cook's Notes

Amount Per Serving	
Calories	101.82
Calories From Fat (22%)	22.26
	% Daily Value
Total Fat 2.6g	4%
Saturated Fat 0.58g	3%
Cholesterol 0mg	0%
Sodium 127.07mg	5%
Potassium 483.74mg	14%
Total Carbohydrates 18.93g	6%
Fiber 2.81g	11%
Sugar 12.56g	
Protein 1.83g	4%

These were tough! For a long time it was seafood only and even that was limited to sea bass, scallops and crab. I used finely chopped mushrooms in lieu of ground meat in a lot of my meals but gradually included a little meat along with the mushrooms. Chicken came much later and only dark meat had sufficient internal moisture.

Sausage Stuffed Portobello Mushrooms (page 83)

Baked Potato with Meat Sauce (page 71)

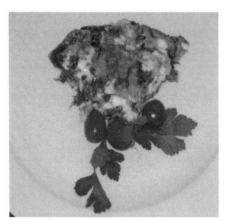

Swiss Chard Pie (page 89)

Spaghetti Squash with Mushroom Balls (page 86)

The humble potato, what would we do without it? This is very satisfying on a cold winter's night.

1	tsp	olive oil	1/2	tsp	minced garlic
3/4	cup	chopped mushrooms	Salt and freshly ground pepper to taste		
1/4	lb	ground beef	1	cup	vodka sauce (or regular spaghetti sauce)
1/2	medium	onion, chopped	1 medium		potato, baked and kept hot
			Grated Parmesan for serving		

Procedure

1. In a medium-size skillet, heat olive oil over medium high heat. Add mushrooms and sauté until slightly browned.
2. Add ground beef and sauté until meat is no longer pink, about 8 minutes. Use a potato masher to break meat apart as it cooks.
3. Add onions, garlic and season with salt and freshly ground pepper. Continue to cook until onions are soft, about 5 minutes.
4. Pour in the vodka sauce and simmer on low heat for another 5 minutes until flavors combine.
5. To serve, cut the hot potato length wise, score flesh with a small knife and pour the sauce. Garnish with grated Parmesan and serve.

Servings: 1

Preparation Time: 25 minutes
Cooking Time: 1 hour

Nutrition Facts

Cook's Notes

Amount Per Serving	
Calories	520.27
Calories From Fat (22%)	116.81
	% Daily Value
Total Fat 13.05g	20%
Saturated Fat 3.03g	15%
Cholesterol 18.32mg	6%
Sodium 1094.05mg	46%
Potassium 2281.26mg	65%
Total Carbohydrates 86.03g	29%
Fiber 12.81g	51%
Sugar 28.87g	
Protein 17.09g	34%

Recipe Tips

A dollop of sour cream or plain yogurt is a nice topping.

Cauliflower Cheese Pie in Potato-Onion Shell

The onion-potato shell is great for a gluten-free option. This was inspired by Molly Katzen.

For the shell

2	cups	peeled and grated Yukon Gold potatoes (about 2 - 3 potatoes)
1/2	tsp	salt
1/4	cup	grated onion
1	large	egg

For the filling

3	Tbs	unsalted butter
1	cup	onion, chopped
1	clove	garlic, crushed
1	medium	head of cauliflower, cut into small florets
1/4	tsp	dry thyme
1/2	tsp	dry basil
2	large	eggs
1/4	cup	milk
1	cup	grated cheddar cheese
Paprika for dusting		

Procedure

1. Preheat oven to 400°.
2. To make the shell, place grated potatoes into a colander, sprinkle in the salt and toss. Set colander in the sink to drain. Let rest 10 - 15 minutes, then squeeze out and discard excess water. Place squeezed potatoes into a large bowl and set aside.
3. Add the grated onions to the potatoes.
4. In a small mixing bowl, beat egg lightly and pour over potato-onion mixture. Stir to combine.
5. Pat into a pie plate (building up the sides), which has been coated with cooking spray.
6. Bake for 40 - 45 minutes until brown. Remove and turn oven down to 375°.
7. To make the filling, in a large skillet, melt butter on medium heat. Sauté onions and garlic about 5 minutes. Add cauliflower and sprinkle in the thyme and basil. Cover and cook on low heat for about 10 minutes until tender, stirring occasionally.
8. In a small bowl, beat together eggs and milk. Set aside.
9. Spread half the cheese into baked shell, layer on cauliflower mixture, top with remaining cheese and pour the egg-milk mixture carefully over everything. Dust the top with paprika and bake for 40 - 45 minutes until set and lightly brown.

Servings: 6
Preparation Time: 30 minutes
Cooking Time: 1 hour and 30 minutes
Nutrition Facts
Serving size: 1/6 of pie

Cook's Notes

Amount Per Serving	
Calories	242.02
Calories From Fat (54%)	130.69
	% Daily Value
Total Fat 14.8g	23%
Saturated Fat 8.62g	43%
Cholesterol 129.06mg	43%
Sodium 361.48mg	15%
Potassium 546.61mg	16%
Total Carbohydrates 17.98g	6%
Fiber 1.85g	7%
Sugar 2.45g	
Protein 10.29g	21%

My friend Tyrell Lewis from London gave me this recipe. It freezes well and the veggies can be varied.

8	chicken thighs, boneless, skinless	2 medium	onions, coarsely chopped
Salt and pepper to taste		1 cup	baby carrots, sliced thick
1 cup	orange marmalade (about 10 oz. jar)	12 oz	red potatoes, halved or quartered
1/4 cup	tamari soy sauce	8 oz	button mushrooms, halved or quartered
1 Tbs	orange zest	Couscous, rice, or pasta for serving	
2 medium	oranges, juiced		

Procedure

1. Salt and pepper chicken thighs generously.
2. In a medium-size bowl, whisk together marmalade, tamari soy sauce, zest and orange juice. Set aside.
3. In a large non-stick skillet which has been coated with cooking spray, brown chicken on both sides, remove to a plate and cover to keep warm.
4. In the same skillet, cook onions, mushrooms until mushrooms give off their liquid and start to brown, 8 minutes. Add carrots, potatoes and marmalade mixture to the skillet.
5. Nestle in chicken thighs and any juices which may have accumulated. Cover and simmer over low heat until chicken and vegetables are very tender, 30 - 35 minutes, stirring occasionally.
6. Serve over couscous, rice or pasta.

Servings: 4

Preparation Time: 15 minutes
Cooking Time: 30 minutes

Nutrition Facts

Serving size: 2 chicken thighs

Cook's Notes

Amount Per Serving	
Calories	738.16
Calories From Fat (8%)	55.74
	% Daily Value
Total Fat 6.23g	10%
Saturated Fat 1.51g	8%
Cholesterol 114.54mg	38%
Sodium 257.88mg	11%
Potassium 2766.64mg	79%
Total Carbohydrates 138.88g	46%
Fiber 11.77g	47%
Sugar 51.65g	
Protein 38.48g	77%

Chicken Salsa

This is one of my easy "go to" recipes. I always have salsa and it takes no time to put together. It goes really well with mashed potatoes and baby peas which you can make while the chicken bakes.

4   chicken thighs, (bone in skin off), or 6   boneless, skinless thighs

Salt and black pepper to taste

8 oz   mild salsa (your favorite brand)
Chopped parsley or cilantro for garnish

Procedure

1 Preheat oven to 375˚.

2 Pat chicken thighs dry and season with salt and freshly ground pepper on both sides.

3 Arrange thighs in a shallow baking dish, pour on the salsa and bake until tender, 30 - 35 minutes.

4 Serve topped with the chopped parsley or cilantro.

Servings: 2

Preparation Time: 5 minutes
Cooking Time: 30 minutes

Nutrition Facts

Serving size: 2 bone in chicken thighs, or 3 boneless

Amount Per Serving	
Calories	199.19
Calories From Fat (25%)	50.4
	% Daily Value
Total Fat 5.6g	9%
Saturated Fat 1.42g	7%
Cholesterol 114.54mg	38%
Sodium 895.68mg	37%
Potassium 703.4mg	20%
Total Carbohydrates 8.11g	3%
Fiber 2.07g	8%
Sugar 3.96g	
Protein 29.11g	58%

Cook's Notes

Recipe Tips

Use fish (catfish, tilapia, cod or halibut) if swallowing chicken is too difficult. Decrease the cooking time accordingly.

The curry powder is flavorful yet mild.

1/2	lb	ground chicken or turkey	1/2	tsp	cinnamon
1/4	cup	chopped onion	1/2	tsp	pumpkin pie spice
3		garlic cloves, minced	Salt and freshly ground black pepper to taste		
1	tsp	curry powder	Water or chicken broth to moisten		
			Salt and pepper to taste		

Procedure

1 Cook ground chicken in a little water until no longer pink, breaking the chicken apart as it cooks (a potato masher works well here).

2 Add remaining ingredients and simmer for 10 - 15 minutes until flavors blend. Add salt and pepper to taste.

Servings: 2

Preparation Time: 10 minutes
Cooking Time: 20 minutes

Nutrition Facts

Serving size: about 1 cup

Cook's Notes

Amount Per Serving	
Calories	134.13
Calories From Fat (19%)	25.21
	% Daily Value
Total Fat 2.81g	4%
Saturated Fat 0.63g	3%
Cholesterol 63.5mg	21%
Sodium 117.47mg	5%
Potassium 435.43mg	12%
Total Carbohydrates 4.76g	2%
Fiber 1.17g	5%
Sugar 0.97g	
Protein 21.75g	44%

Latin Lasagna ⅔₄

The plantain is a brilliant alternative to pasta. Thank you to Ingrid Hoffman on Food Channel.

1/2	stick	unsalted butter
1	medium	onion, finely chopped

Salt and pepper to taste

1/3	cup	all-purpose flour
1	Tbs	ground cumin
2	cups	free-range, low-sodium chicken broth
1	cup	heavy (whipping) cream
2	cups	shredded Monterey pepper jack cheese, divided

6 oz		raw chorizo sausage, casing removed
1 lb		ground chicken or turkey
2 Tbs		Worcestershire sauce
1 Tbs		fresh lemon juice
1 tsp		dried oregano
4		plantains, (large, raw, black) halved, peeled and thinly sliced lengthwise
		Paprika for garnish, (optional)

Procedure

1 Preheat oven to 350°. Coat a 9 x 12" baking dish with non-stick cooking spray. Set aside.

2 In a medium-size saucepan, melt butter over medium heat. Add onions, season with salt and pepper and sauté until translucent, about 5 minutes.

3 Stir in flour and cumin and cook stirring for about 1 minute. Pour in broth, whisking to prevent lumps. Add cream and continue to cook, whisking until sauce is thick and smooth, 8 - 10 minutes.

4 Stir in 1/2 of cheese until melted. Remove from stove, cover surface of sauce with cling wrap to prevent skin from forming.

5 In a large skillet over medium high heat add chorizo breaking it up with a potato masher. Add ground chicken (or turkey) and cook stirring and breaking up meat until no longer pink, 8 - 10 minutes. Drain excess fat if necessary, add Worcestershire, lemon juice, and oregano, and season with salt and pepper to taste.

6 Divide plantain slices into 3 batches. Line bottom of baking dish with first layer of plantains to cover in a single layer. Top plantains with half of meat mixture, spreading in an even layer to cover. Top with half of the cheese sauce, spreading evenly with a spatula.

7 Add another layer of plantain slices to cover cheese sauce, spread remaining meat mixture evenly, and cover with remaining cheese sauce.

8 Add final layer of plantain slices, sprinkle remaining shredded cheese to cover. Sprinkle with paprika, if using, and bake for 45 minutes to 1 hour until cheese is bubbly and brown. Allow to cool 5 minutes before cutting and serving.

Servings: 8 Preparation   Time: 30 minutes   Cooking Time: 1 hour

Nutrition Facts

Serving size: 1/8 of lasagna

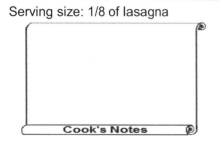

Cook's Notes

Amount Per Serving	
Calories	537.9
Calories From Fat (48%)	259.7
	% Daily Value
Total Fat 28.89g	44%
Saturated Fat 14g	70%
Cholesterol 114.53mg	38%
Sodium 556.69mg	23%
Potassium 675.89mg	19%
Total Carbohydrates 38.73g	13%
Fiber 2.65g	11%
Sugar 16.21g	
Protein 32.7g	65%

This is from the Moosewood Cookbook. It was published in 1977. Mine is falling apart but I still love it and use it often. And by the way, real men do eat quiche!

1		9-inch pie shell, unbaked	1 1/2	cups	buttermilk
1 1/2	cups	grated gruyère cheese, (or other mild cheese)	4	large	eggs, beaten, (or 3/4 cup egg white)
2	Tbs	unsalted butter	3	Tbs	flour
1	cup	thinly sliced scallions, (white part and tips of green part)	1/4	tsp	salt
			1/4	tsp	dry mustard
4	oz	sliced mushrooms	1/2	tsp	prepared horseradish
1/4	tsp	dried thyme			

Procedure

1. Preheat oven to 375°.
2. Scatter grated cheese on the bottom of pie shell evenly.
3. In a medium skillet, melt butter and sauté scallions and mushrooms until tender, about 10 minutes. Crumble dried thyme between your fingers to release their flavor and sprinkle over onions. Season with a little salt and pepper. Arrange mixture on top of cheese.
4. In a blender, purée buttermilk, eggs, flour, salt, mustard and horseradish. Pour mixture over mushroom-cheese mixture. Place pie on a baking sheet; bake for 40 - 45 minutes or until set.

Servings: 6

Preparation Time: 15 minutes
Cooking Time: 45 minutes

Nutrition Facts

Serving size: 1/6 of quiche

Cook's Notes

Amount Per Serving	
Calories	423.61
Calories From Fat (56%)	238.77
	% Daily Value
Total Fat 26.83g	41%
Saturated Fat 13.03g	65%
Cholesterol 168.78mg	56%
Sodium 447.35mg	19%
Potassium 300.27mg	9%
Total Carbohydrates 28.5g	10%
Fiber 1.33g	5%
Sugar 4.67g	
Protein 17.14g	34%

These are very moist and it's better to use a knife and fork and not a bun.

3	Tbs	olive oil, divided	3/4	cup	Panko or dry bread crumbs
1 1/2	lb	mushrooms coarsely chopped (such as Portobello, crimini, shitake, or button)	2	large	eggs ,lightly beaten
			1	Tbs	parsley, chopped
			1	tsp	dried basil leaves
1	medium	sweet onion, grated	3/4	tsp	salt
3	tsp	minced garlic	1/4	tsp	black pepper
2/3	cup	quinoa flakes			
1/3	cup	shredded Parmigiano-Reggiano cheese			

Procedure

1. In a large non-stick skillet, heat 1 tablespoon of oil on medium high heat. Sauté onion, mushrooms and garlic until mushrooms give off their liquid and start to brown, about 10 minutes. Remove from heat and transfer to a large bowl.
2. Add remaining ingredients (except remaining olive oil) and mix well to combine. Set aside to cool for about 15 minutes.
3. Divide cooled mixture into 4 equal parts. Shape each piece into a patty.
4. Heat remaining 2 tablespoons of olive oil in the same skillet. Brown patties for about 5 minutes per side or until golden brown.
5. Serve with your favorite toppings such as sliced tomatoes, onions, relish, etc.

Servings: 4

Preparation Time: 15 minutes
Cooking Time: 15 minutes

Nutrition Facts

Serving size: 1 burger patty

Cook's Notes

Amount Per Serving	
Calories	288.49
Calories From Fat (49%)	140.41
	% Daily Value
Total Fat 15.9g	24%
Saturated Fat 3.73g	19%
Cholesterol 100.33mg	33%
Sodium 627.39mg	26%
Potassium 650.8mg	19%
Total Carbohydrates 23.97g	8%
Fiber 4.31g	17%
Sugar 5.45g	
Protein 15.12g	30%

The Portobello mushrooms give this dish a meaty flavor with a much softer texture. You won't miss the meat.

1	Tbs	olive oil		1	Tbs	flour
2	Tbs	unsalted butter		3/4	cups	crème fraîche (or sour cream)
1 medium		yellow onion, finely diced		1 1/2	Tbs	chopped fresh dill sprigs
4 large		portobello mushroom caps, diced		1/2	Tbs	Worcestershire sauce
1	cup	free-range, low-sodium beef stock		Salt and pepper to taste		

Procedure

1. In a large skillet heat butter and oil on medium-high heat. Add onion and sauté until wilted, about 3 minutes.
2. Add mushrooms and brown stirring occasionally for 8 minutes. Add Worcestershire sauce, salt and pepper to taste and stir in the beef stock. Sauté for 5 minutes.
3. When mushrooms are tender, blend flour and crème fraîche (or sour cream) to a smooth paste and gently stir into the simmering mushrooms.
4. Add chopped fresh dill and season to taste.

Servings: 4

Preparation Time: 30 minutes
Cooking Time: 20 minutes

Nutrition Facts

Serving size: about 1 cup

Cook's Notes

Amount Per Serving	
Calories	335.54
Calories From Fat (60%)	200.87
	% Daily Value
Total Fat 22.82g	35%
Saturated Fat 12.24g	61%
Cholesterol 55.39mg	18%
Sodium 213.64mg	9%
Potassium 415.88mg	12%
Total Carbohydrates 28.53g	10%
Fiber 4.08g	16%
Sugar 2.71g	
Protein 7.48g	15%

This is a simple Hungarian casserole using boiled sliced potatoes. By using shredded frozen potatoes it is faster and much easier to swallow. It can easily be made vegetarian by omitting the kielbasa (a Polish Sausage).

2 Tbs	unsalted butter, divided		4		hard-boiled eggs, thinly sliced
1 large	onion, thinly sliced		12	oz	Polish kielbasa, thinly sliced
1 tsp	salt		1	cup	sour cream
Ground pepper to taste			Dash of paprika (Hungarian sweet)		
2 cups	frozen shredded raw potatoes				

Procedure

1 Preheat oven to 375°. Butter a 1 1/2 quart square casserole dish with 1 tablespoon of the butter and set aside.

2 In a large skillet, melt remaining 1 tablespoon of butter, add onions and cook on low heat until caramelized, 20 - 25 minutes. Season with the salt and pepper to taste.

3 Assemble: Layer half the frozen potatoes on bottom of casserole dish, spread with half the onion mixture, 1/2 of the egg slices, 1/2 of the sausage slices, and 1/2 of the sour cream. Repeat layers finishing with sour cream to cover and sprinkle with paprika.

4 Bake 45 minutes until potatoes are very tender when a skewer is inserted. Allow to rest for 5 - 10 minutes before serving.

Servings: 4

Preparation Time: 30 minutes
Cooking Time: 45 minutes

Nutrition Facts

Serving size: about 1 ½ cups

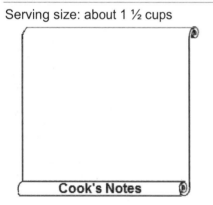

Cook's Notes

Amount Per Serving	
Calories	732.17
Calories From Fat (65%)	476.23
	% Daily Value
Total Fat 53.41g	82%
Saturated Fat 22.78g	114%
Cholesterol 374.91mg	125%
Sodium 2739.46mg	114%
Potassium 515.06mg	15%
Total Carbohydrates 31.26g	10%
Fiber 2.19g	9%
Sugar 4.36g	
Protein 33.03g	66%

This is a satisfying light dish.

1 (15-oz)		can unsweetened pumpkin puree (or cooked butternut squash)
1	Tbs	olive oil
1/2	cup	chopped onion
1		garlic clove, minced
1/2	tsp	ground cumin
1/4	tsp	ground coriander
1/4	tsp	smoked paprika

3/4	cup	chopped roasted red peppers
1/2	tsp	salt
Freshly ground black pepper		
2	cups	frozen corn kernels
2	large	eggs, lightly beaten
1	cup	grated cheddar or Monterey Jack cheese

Procedure

1. Scoop pumpkin purée into a large bowl.
2. In a medium-size skillet heat the olive oil on medium high heat. Sauté onions, garlic and spices until onions are translucent and spices are fragrant, about 8 minutes.
3. Add roasted peppers, salt and black pepper, and simmer for another 5 minutes. Add to pumpkin, with corn and eggs and mix well.
4. Spread mixture into a 2 quart casserole dish which has been coated with cooking spray and top with the cheese. Cover with foil.
5. Bake 20 minutes, uncover and bake an additional 15 minutes until a skewers inserted in center comes out clean.

Servings: 4

Preparation Time: 15 minutes
Cooking Time: 35 minutes

Nutrition Facts

Serving size: ¼ recipe about 10 oz.

Cook's Notes

Amount Per Serving	
Calories	301.59
Calories From Fat (47%)	142.41
	% Daily Value
Total Fat 16.16g	25%
Saturated Fat 7.46g	37%
Cholesterol 122.66mg	41%
Sodium 1000.87mg	42%
Potassium 577.83mg	17%
Total Carbohydrates 29.33g	10%
Fiber 6.39g	26%
Sugar 7.69g	
Protein 14.12g	28%

The biscuit mix makes almost a custard-type consistency and the soft vegetables give it just the right mouth feel.

2	Tbs	unsalted butter	1/4	tsp	black pepper
1	Tbs	olive oil	1/2	tsp	dried basil, crushed
1	cup	chopped zucchini	1/4	tsp	dried thyme leaves, crushed
1	cup	peeled and diced eggplant	1	cup	shredded Monterey Jack cheese
1/2	cup	chopped onion			
1 medium		garlic clove, minced	1 1/2	cups	milk
1/2	cup	chopped roasted red peppers	1/4	cup	sour cream or plain yogurt
1/2	cup	chopped tomatoes	3/4	cup	biscuit mix
3/4	tsp	salt	3	large	eggs

Procedure

1 Preheat oven 400°. Coat a deep dish pie plate with cooking spray. Set aside.

2 In a large skillet over medium high heat, melt butter and olive oil together. Add vegetables and cook, stirring, until crisp-tender, 8 - 10 minutes. Add seasonings and stir until well combined.

3 Spread vegetable mixture on bottom of pie plate and sprinkle with cheese.

4 Combine remaining ingredients in a blender and process on high for about 1 minute.

5 Pour into pie plate, set pie plate on a baking sheet and bake for 35 - 40 minutes until pie sets. Allow to cool for 5 minutes before serving.

Servings: 6

Preparation Time: 20 minutes
Cooking Time: 35 minutes

Nutrition Facts

Serving size: 1/6 of pie

Cook's Notes

Amount Per Serving	
Calories	279.72
Calories From Fat (57%)	159.2
	% Daily Value
Total Fat 18.02g	28%
Saturated Fat 8.62g	43%
Cholesterol 125.73mg	42%
Sodium 619.09mg	26%
Potassium 348.46mg	10%
Total Carbohydrates 17.52g	6%
Fiber 1.67g	7%
Sugar 7.87g	
Protein 12.36g	25%

Portobello mushrooms are a great for stuffing things into. The sausage mixed with the cottage cheese makes it a substantial main course.

2 large	portobello mushrooms, stems and gills removed	2	Tbs	Parmesan
		2	Tbs	cottage cheese
		1/2	cup	tomato sauce
4 oz	raw sweet Italian sausage, casing removed	1	Tbs	heavy (whipping) cream

Procedure

1 Preheat oven to 350°.

2 Clean mushrooms and place on a foil lined baking sheet which has been coated with cooking spray. Bake for 10 - 15 minutes, until just starting to get soft. Remove from the oven and cool slightly.

3 Meanwhile, in a non-stick skillet, brown the sausage, breaking up the meat with a wooden spoon, drain, and remove to a bowl to cool slightly. Mix in the cheeses and spoon into warm mushroom caps.

4 Bake at 350° for about 20 minutes.

5 In a small sauce pan gently heat the tomato sauce with the cream.

6 Place mushrooms on serving plates, spoon the tomato sauce over and sprinkle with additional cheese.

Servings: 2

Preparation Time: 10 minutes
Cooking Time: 30 minutes

Nutrition Facts

Serving size: 1 mushroom cap

Cook's Notes

Amount Per Serving	
Calories	227.86
Calories From Fat (62%)	140.81
	% Daily Value
Total Fat 15.94g	25%
Saturated Fat 5.81g	29%
Cholesterol 60.44mg	20%
Sodium 844.28mg	35%
Potassium 538.11mg	15%
Total Carbohydrates 8.52g	3%
Fiber 2.04g	8%
Sugar 5.32g	
Protein 14.87g	30%

This belongs in the comfort food category.

1	lb	Yukon Gold potatoes, peeled and cubed	1		bay leaf
1/2	cup	heavy (whipping) cream	4	oz	sliced mushrooms
1	Tbs	unsalted butter	1	Tbs	tomato paste
Freshly grated nutmeg			2	Tbs	all-purpose flour
1 1/2	tsp	salt, divided	1	tsp	Worcestershire sauce
3/4	tsp	black pepper, divided	1/4	tsp	liquid smoke (optional)
1	Tbs	olive oil	1 1/4	cup	beef broth
1	lb	ground beef (lamb, turkey or chicken)	1 1/2	cups	frozen peas and carrots
1	large	onion chopped	1/2	cup	grated sharp cheddar cheese
1	tsp	smoked paprika (optional)			

Procedure

1 Preheat oven to 400°. Coat a 2 1/2 quart casserole dish with cooking spray and set aside.

2 Place potatoes in a medium sauce pan and cover with water by 1-inch. Bring to a boil, reduce heat and simmer until fork tender, 15 - 20 minutes. Drain and return to pot. Over very low heat, mash with a potato masher, adding the heavy cream, butter, nutmeg, 1/2 tsp salt, and 1/4 tsp pepper. Stir until smooth and creamy.

3 Meanwhile, heat olive oil in a large skillet over medium high heat add ground beef and cook breaking up the meat until starting to brown, about 5 minutes.

4 Add onions, 1 teaspoon of salt, smoked paprika (if using), 1/2 teaspoon pepper and bay leaf and cook stirring for 2 - 3 minutes.

5 Add mushrooms and sauté until liquid is released from mushrooms, about 4 minutes. Add tomato paste and cook, stirring, until fragrant,1 to 2 minutes.

6 Sprinkle in flour and cook, stirring 1 minute. Add Worcestershire and liquid smoke (if using) to beef broth and gradually pour over meat mixture while stirring. Bring to a boil, reduce the heat to low, cover, and simmer until thickened, 20 to 25 minutes.

7 Pour meat mixture into casserole dish. Arrange peas and carrot mixture over meat mixture.

8 Top with mashed potatoes to almost cover (leave about 1/2" border), sprinkle with cheese. Place casserole dish on a baking sheet (to prevent bubbling over).

9 Bake for 10 - 15 minutes or until cheese melts and is slightly brown.

Servings: 4   Preparation Time: 15 minutes   Cooking Time: 30 minutes

Nutrition Facts

Serving size: 1 ½ cups

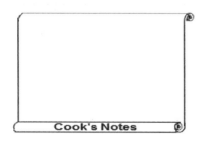

Cook's Notes

Amount Per Serving	
Calories	434.5
Calories From Fat (51%)	223.25
	% Daily Value
Total Fat 25.18g	39%
Saturated Fat 10.73g	54%
Cholesterol 65.27mg	22%
Sodium 1493.64mg	62%
Potassium 1200.51mg	34%
Total Carbohydrates 40.72g	14%
Fiber 4.59g	18%
Sugar 3.07g	
Protein 14.43g	29%

Slumgullion ½

My first introduction to Slumgullion was when I lived in Ottawa, Canada. It was the family favorite of Paul Friesen who was a father figure to me in my early twenties. It is usually a combination of ground beef, tomatoes, tomato sauce and macaroni, however Paul made his version more like a Shepherd's Pie using mashed potatoes to top the dish after he combined ground beef with spaghetti sauce and layered it with yellow waxed beans. My adaptation uses baby bella mushrooms instead of ground meat but I kept the beans and mashed potatoes because they are easy to swallow.

2		russet potatoes, peeled and diced
1/4	cup	heavy (whipping) cream, warmed
1	Tbs	unsalted butter, plus more for dotting
1	Tbs	olive oil
1/2	cup	chopped onion

8 oz minced mushrooms, (baby bellas)
1 cup vodka sauce (or regular spaghetti sauce)
Salt and pepper to taste
1 (14.5 oz) can yellow or green beans, drained and rinsed
Dash of paprika

Procedure

1 Preheat oven to 375°.

2 Boil the potatoes in salted water until tender, 15 - 20 minutes. Drain and mash with warm cream, until very smooth.

3 In a 10 inch skillet, melt the butter with the olive oil on medium high heat. Sauté onions until translucent, about 8 minutes, add mushrooms and cook until soft, 8 - 10 minutes longer.

4 Stir in the vodka or spaghetti sauce and season to taste with salt and pepper. Cook gently for a few minutes over low heat. Pour into a 1 1/2 quart casserole dish.

5 Spread beans over mushroom mixture. Carefully top with mashed potatoes smoothing the top to the edge of casserole dish. Dot with a few bits of butter and sprinkle with paprika.

6 Bake for 20 - 25 minutes uncovered until slightly browned. Cool for 5 minutes before serving.

Preparation Time: 20 minutes   Cooking Time: 30 minutes

Nutrition Facts

Serving size: about 1 cup

Cook's Notes

Amount Per Serving	
Calories	224.81
Calories From Fat (54%)	121.4
	% Daily Value
Total Fat 13.75g	21%
Saturated Fat 6.22g	31%
Cholesterol 29.3mg	10%
Sodium 367.69mg	15%
Potassium 571.11mg	16%
Total Carbohydrates 22.85g	8%
Fiber 3.88g	16%
Sugar 8.47g	
Protein 4.31g	9%

I like to use Nate's Savory Mushroom Meatless Meatballs, available at Whole Foods. They are very easy to swallow and taste great. The meatballs are not included in the nutritional facts. Three meatless balls are 100 calories.

1	small	spaghetti squash, cut in half, seeds removed	6 prepared meatballs (see above) Parmesan cheese for serving
1 1/2	cups	vodka sauce (or regular spaghetti sauce)	

Procedure

1. Preheat oven to 400°.
2. Lay the squash cut side down on a baking sheet that has been lined with foil and coated with cooking spray. Bake for about 45 minutes, or until soft.
3. In a medium-size saucepan, heat the sauce with the meatballs gently until warm, 15 - 20 minutes.
4. When squash is done, fluff the spaghetti-like fibers scraping crosswise with a fork. Remove strands to serving plates, top each serving with 3 meatballs, spoon over the sauce and serve with a pinch of cheese.

Servings: 2

Preparation Time: 10 minutes
Cooking Time: 45 minutes

Nutrition Facts

Serving size: ½ squash with 3 meatballs and ½ of sauce

Cook's Notes

Amount Per Serving	
Calories	239.25
Calories From Fat (27%)	65.08
	% Daily Value
Total Fat 7.2g	11%
Saturated Fat 1.86g	9%
Cholesterol 5.14mg	2%
Sodium 1062.29mg	44%
Potassium 866.66mg	25%
Total Carbohydrates 38.85g	13%
Fiber 6.68g	27%
Sugar 22.72g	
Protein 4.9g	10%

This is a simple casserole using biscuit mix.

1	cup	biscuit mix	4	oz	smoked gouda, grated
1/4	cup	chicken broth	12	oz	cottage cheese
4	large	eggs, divided (2 for biscuit mix, 2	2		garlic cloves, crushed
		for spinach mixture)	1	tsp	Italian seasoning
1/4	cup	onion, finely diced	Freshly grated nutmeg		
1 (10 oz)		package frozen chopped spinach, thawed and squeezed dry			
1/2	cup	grated Parmesan cheese			

Procedure

1. Preheat oven to 375°.
2. Coat a 12 x 7 1/2 x 2 inch baking dish with cooking spray.
3. In a medium-size bowl, mix baking mix, chicken broth, 2 eggs, and onions, beating vigorously about 20 strokes.
4. Spread into baking dish.
5. In a large bowl, mix remaining ingredients and spoon evenly over baking mixture. Bake for 30 minutes or until casserole sets.
6. Cool for 5 minutes before cutting into squares.

Servings: 8

Preparation Time: 15 minutes
Cooking Time: 35 minutes

Nutrition Facts

Serving size: about 1 cup

Cook's Notes

Amount Per Serving	
Calories	230.76
Calories From Fat (45%)	104.35
	% Daily Value
Total Fat 11.83g	18%
Saturated Fat 5.49g	27%
Cholesterol 119.82mg	40%
Sodium 631.82mg	26%
Potassium 223.79mg	6%
Total Carbohydrates 14.3g	5%
Fiber 1.47g	6%
Sugar 4.53g	
Protein 16.78g	34%

This is very pretty served on top of whole wheat couscous.

2 large	bell peppers (red, yellow, or orange)	
3	scallions, thinly sliced	
4 medium	mushrooms, chopped	
1 Tbs	sun dried tomatoes, drained of oil and minced	

1	Tbs	chopped fresh parsley
1/4	cup	canned beans, (preferably butter beans)
4	Tbs	chopped dried apricots
Salt and pepper to taste		
2	Tbs	grated Parmesan cheese

Procedure

1. Preheat oven to 375°. Put the kettle on for boiling hot water.
2. Cut the peppers in half and discard seeds and ribs. Place pepper halves in a heat proof dish and cover with boiling water. Cover with foil, let stand for 10 minutes, drain water carefully and set aside.
3. In a medium-size bowl combine remaining ingredients, except cheese. Season with salt and pepper to taste and spoon mixture into pepper halves, topping with grated cheese.
4. Pour about 2 inches of boiling hot water carefully around peppers, cover loosely with foil and bake for 25 minutes or until peppers are soft.
5. Using tongs, carefully lift peppers onto serving plates.

Servings: 2

Preparation Time: 30 minutes
Cooking Time: 30 minutes

Nutrition Facts

Serving size: 2 pepper halves

Cook's Notes

Amount Per Serving	
Calories	271.46
Calories From Fat (9%)	24.32
	% Daily Value
Total Fat 2.79g	4%
Saturated Fat 1.06g	5%
Cholesterol 4.4mg	1%
Sodium 152.41mg	6%
Potassium 1712.58mg	49%
Total Carbohydrates 51.27g	17%
Fiber 13.68g	55%
Sugar 20.88g	
Protein 15.51g	31%

You can also substitute baby spinach for the Swiss chard.

1 Tbs	extra-virgin olive oil	3 large	eggs
3	thick slices bacon, chopped	8 oz	crème fraîche (or sour cream)
1 small	onion, finely chopped	Salt and pepper to taste	
1	garlic clove, minced	4 oz	gruyère cheese, grated
1 bunch	Swiss chard, kale or mustard greens	1 handful	dried cranberries (or raisins)
		1 handful	toasted pine nuts
		1	prepared 9-inch pie crust, unbaked

Procedure

1 Preheat oven to 375°.

2 In a large non-stick sauté pan, heat olive oil on medium heat. Add the bacon and cook until crisp, 4 - 5 minutes. Add onions and garlic and cook stirring until onion is translucent, 3 - 4 minutes. Remove to a plate and reserve.

3 Pull chard leaves from stems by placing your fingers (one on each side) along the stem and pulling away. Discard stems. Thinly shred leaves.

4 Add chard leaves to the pan, wilt leaves in the bacon fat and any water clinging to leaves stirring and turning, about 5 minutes. To speed the process, turn the heat to low and cover the pan for a few minutes.

5 In a one-quart measuring cup, beat eggs together with crème fraîche. Season with salt and pepper.

6 In a large bowl, combine and toss all ingredients until well combined, except the egg mixture. Fill pie shell with chard mixture, then carefully pour egg mixture over. Set on a baking sheet and bake until pie sets, 30 - 35 minutes. Allow to cool a bit before slicing and serving.

Servings: 8

Preparation Time: 15 minutes
Cooking Time: 45 minutes

Nutrition Facts

Serving size: 1/8 of pie

Cook's Notes

Amount Per Serving	
Calories	528.96
Calories From Fat (70%)	372.79
	% Daily Value
Total Fat 42.51g	65%
Saturated Fat 13.89g	69%
Cholesterol 120.96mg	40%
Sodium 315.99mg	13%
Potassium 267.18mg	8%
Total Carbohydrates 25.82g	9%
Fiber 1.94g	8%
Sugar 1.36g	
Protein 13.09g	26%

This one I owe to Rachael Ray. I've never been a big fan of polenta but this is so creamy and yummy that it's an ingredient I'll use more often.

2	Tbs	olive oil	1	cup	heavy (whipping) cream, divided
1	lb	chicken thighs, boneless, skinless, and chopped	1/2	cup	quick-cooking polenta
1/2	lb	chicken tenders, chopped	1	cup	grated gruyère cheese
2	medium	carrots, chopped	2	Tbs	unsalted butter
1	medium	onion, chopped	2	Tbs	unbleached white flour
2	ribs	celery, chopped	2	tsp	Dijon mustard
Salt and freshly ground black pepper to taste			4	Tbs	chopped fresh tarragon
3	cups	chicken broth, divided	1	cup	frozen baby peas

Procedure

1 In a deep skillet heat extra-virgin olive oil over medium high heat. Lightly brown chicken, about 3 minutes. Add carrots, onion, and celery, season with salt and pepper and cook 10 to 12 minutes until vegetables soften.

2 Preheat broiler and set rack to center of oven.

3 In a medium-size sauce pan, bring 1 cup chicken broth and 1/2 cup cream to a boil, stir in polenta and whisk continuously for 3 minutes. Turn heat to low, stir in gruyere cheese and reserve.

4 Move chicken and veggie mixture off to side of skillet, melt butter and sprinkle in flour, and stir for 1 minute. Whisk in 2 cups remaining chicken stock and combine well. Stir in 1/2 cup remaining cream and bring to a boil. Stir in Dijon mustard, tarragon, frozen peas, and adjust salt and pepper.

5 Divide mixture into serving bowls and set bowls on baking sheet. Top pot pies with polenta mixture, and broil until brown, 2 to 3 minutes.

6 Allow to cool slightly before serving.

Servings: 4

Preparation Time: 15 minutes
Cooking Time: 30 minutes

Nutrition Facts

Serving size: 1 pot pie

Cook's Notes

Amount Per Serving	
Calories	805.24
Calories From Fat (56%)	448.58
	% Daily Value
Total Fat 50.73g	78%
Saturated Fat 25g	125%
Cholesterol 225.73mg	75%
Sodium 462.35mg	19%
Potassium 624.58mg	18%
Total Carbohydrates 46.1g	15%
Fiber 6.99g	28%
Sugar 4.92g	
Protein 40.29g	81%

Tofu Loaf

An old Tofu Cookery book was the idea for this loaf. It keeps its flavor for several days and reheats well.

2 (14 oz)		containers medium-hard tofu, drained and crumbled	1/4	tsp	black pepper
			1	medium	onion, chopped
1/2	cup	ketchup	1/4	tsp	garlic powder
1/3	cup	tamari soy sauce	1	cup	Panko or other dry bread crumbs
2	Tbs	Dijon mustard			
1/2	cup	chopped fresh parsley			

Procedure

1. Mix all ingredients together in a large bowl.
2. Coat an 8 or 9 inch loaf pan with cooking spray and press mixture into pan. Tap a few times on the counter to release any air bubbles.
3. Bake for about an hour edges start to pull away side of loaf pan. Let cool 10 minutes in pan before slicing.
4. Garnish with additional ketchup and parsley, if desired.

Servings: 8
Yield: 1 medium loaf

Preparation Time: 10 minutes
Cooking Time: 1 hour
Inactive Time: 10 minutes

Nutrition Facts

Serving size: 1/8 of loaf

Cook's Notes

Amount Per Serving	
Calories	66.55
Calories From Fat (23%)	15.52
	% Daily Value
Total Fat 1.85g	3%
Saturated Fat 0.22g	1%
Cholesterol 0mg	0%
Sodium 115.34mg	5%
Potassium 80.71mg	2%
Total Carbohydrates 9.23g	3%
Fiber 1.49g	6%
Sugar 0.88g	
Protein 4.34g	9%

Tomato Basil Chicken

Although the ingredients sound exotic it is a lovely dish and not spicy in the least – just flavorful.

8	chicken thighs, boneless, skinless	2 small	cinnamon sticks
Salt and pepper to taste		2 whole	star anise
2 Tbs	unrefined coconut oil*	1/2 inch	piece fresh ginger, sliced
1 medium	sweet onion, thinly sliced	1 1/2 cups	coarsely chopped fresh basil
1 (14 oz)	can diced tomatoes with liquid		

Procedure

1 Season chicken with salt and pepper.

2 In a large skillet, heat 1 tablespoon of coconut oil on medium high heat. Brown chicken lightly on both sides, remove and cover to keep warm.

3 Add remaining 1 tablespoon coconut oil to skillet and cook onions until lightly brown, about 5 minutes.

4 Add tomatoes, cinnamon sticks, star anise and ginger. Season with salt and pepper to taste.

5 Nestle chicken pieces into sauce, cover and cook on moderate heat turning chicken once until cooked through, about 20 minutes.

6 Transfer chicken to serving plates. Stir basil into sauce for a minute or so, just until it begins to wilt. Remove cinnamon sticks and star anise, spoon sauce over chicken and serve.

Servings: 4

Preparation Time: 15 minutes
Cooking Time: 20 minutes

Nutrition Facts

Serving size: 2 chicken thighs

Cook's Notes

Amount Per Serving	
Calories	383.1
Calories From Fat (32%)	121.56
	% Daily Value
Total Fat 14.11g	22%
Saturated Fat 2.65g	13%
Cholesterol 114.54mg	38%
Sodium 139.89mg	6%
Potassium 535.83mg	15%
Total Carbohydrates 45.81g	15%
Fiber 28.57g	114%
Sugar 2.65g	
Protein 30.5g	61%

Recipe Tips

I order the coconut oil from CoconutOil-Online.com. It has the best flavor.

Use the Corn "Tortilla" recipe on page 21. This "Tortilla" stays moist where regular corn tortillas are too dry for easy swallowing.

1/2	(14.5 oz)	can black beans (or pinto), drained and rinsed	4		scallions, thinly sliced (white part and tips of green part)
1/2	cup	mild salsa (your favorite brand)	4 large		olives, black or green, sliced
			1/4	cup	grated cheddar cheese
1 1/2	cups	shredded lettuce	1/2	cup	guacamole
1/4	cup	diced tomatoes	1/4	cup	sour cream or plain yogurt

Procedure

1 In a small food processor, puree beans with salsa until smooth.
2 Divide bean mixture among "tortillas" and spread in a layer.
3 Layer remaining ingredients, starting with the lettuce and build your hay stack.
4 Drizzle with additional salsa for additional moisture and flavor.

Servings: 4

Preparation Time: 15 minutes

Nutrition Facts

Serving size: 1 haystack

Cook's Notes

Amount Per Serving	
Calories	133.91
Calories From Fat (47%)	63.25
	% Daily Value
Total Fat 7.48g	12%
Saturated Fat 2.42g	12%
Cholesterol 8.33mg	3%
Sodium 384.45mg	16%
Potassium 482.41mg	14%
Total Carbohydrates 12.71g	4%
Fiber 3.97g	16%
Sugar 3.19g	
Protein 6.12g	12%

From Bobby Flay - this is fabulous! I use quinoa flakes to keep it moist but it still holds its shape for slicing.

2	Tbs	olive oil	1/4	cup	chopped fresh parsley
1	small	zucchini, finely diced	1 1/2	lb	ground beef (lamb, turkey or chicken)
1	medium	red pepper, finely diced			
1	medium	yellow bell pepper, finely diced	1	cup	quinoa flakes
5		garlic cloves, peeled and smashed	1/2	cup	grated Parmesan or Romano cheese
			3/4	cup	ketchup, organic, divided
1/4	tsp	smoked paprika (optional)	1/4	cup plus 2 Tbs balsamic vinegar
				2 - 3 drops Tabasco (optional)

Salt and pepper to taste
1 large egg lightly beaten
1 Tbs fresh, chopped thyme leaves

Procedure

1 Preheat oven to 425°.

2 In a large nonstick skillet, heat oil on medium high heat, add zucchini, peppers, garlic and paprika. Season with salt and pepper and sauté stirring until vegetables are tender, about 5 minutes. Set aside to cool.

3 In a large bowl, whisk the egg with the herbs. Add ground meat, cooled vegetable mixture, quinoa flakes, cheese and 1/2 cup ketchup, & 2 Tbs. balsamic. Mix just until well combined.

4 Press mixture gently into a 9 x 5 inch loaf pan. Whisk together remaining ketchup and 1/4 cup balsamic, adding a few drops of Tabasco if desired. Pour mixture over loaf, smoothing the top to cover evenly.

5 Bake for 1 1/4 hours or until a skewer inserted comes out clean. Let rest 10 minutes before slicing into serving pieces.

Servings: 8

Preparation Time: 30 minutes
Cooking Time: 1 hour and 15 minutes

Nutrition Facts

Serving size: 1/8 of meatloaf

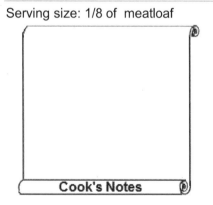

Cook's Notes

Amount Per Serving	
Calories	154.81
Calories From Fat (39%)	60.52
	% Daily Value
Total Fat 6.84g	11%
Saturated Fat 2.15g	11%
Cholesterol 38.63mg	13%
Sodium 372.75mg	16%
Potassium 314.09mg	9%
Total Carbohydrates 14.81g	5%
Fiber 1.36g	5%
Sugar 8.29g	
Protein 8.38g	17%

n the old days I used to make my own but now there are many varieties of pre-made nut milks on the market. I always buy the unsweetened ones because I can control the amount and type of sweetener I use. I love to use coconut milk and coconut water because it's straight from nature.

I have provided a few recipes for you to make your own if you prefer - it's very simple.

Rich Cashew Milk (page 100)

Almond Milk

Soak almonds in water and cover overnight to soften the nuts. When you're ready to make it, drain the soaking water and use fresh water to make the milk.

1/4	cup	slivered almonds
1	cup	water

1 tsp agave nectar (optional)

Procedure

1 Combine drained nuts with fresh water in a blender and process on high speed until well incorporated.

2 Store in a glass jar and refrigerate for up to 3 days.

Servings: 1

Preparation Time: 5 minutes

Nutrition Facts

Serving size: 1 cup

Cook's Notes

Amount Per Serving	
Calories	102.64
Calories From Fat (73%)	75.15
	% Daily Value
Total Fat 8.98g	14%
Saturated Fat 0.7g	4%
Cholesterol 0mg	0%
Sodium 4.07mg	<1%
Potassium 124.01mg	4%
Total Carbohydrates 3.66g	1%
Fiber 1.88g	8%
Sugar 0.85g	
Protein 3.63g	7%

Recipe Tips

For a smoother consistency, strain through a sieve lined with a coffee filter. Discard the solids.

Cashew Milk

Cashew nuts are soft and don't have to be filtered or soaked. For sweetness add a teaspoon of agave nectar or maple syrup to the blender.

1/4	cup	raw cashews	1 tsp agave nectar (optional)
1	cup	water	

Procedure

1 Combine nuts and water in a blender and process on high speed until well incorporated.

2 Store in a glass jar and refrigerate for up to 3 days.

Servings: 1

Preparation Time: 5 minutes

Nutrition Facts

Serving size: 1 cup

Cook's Notes

Amount Per Serving	
Calories	19.6
Calories From Fat (66%)	13
	% Daily Value
Total Fat 1.55g	2%
Saturated Fat 0.28g	1%
Cholesterol 0mg	0%
Sodium 3.98mg	<1%
Potassium 24.57mg	<1%
Total Carbohydrates 1.07g	<1%
Fiber 0.12g	<1%
Sugar 0.21g	
Protein 0.65g	1%

Chocolate Milk

This is a marvelous substitute for anyone who is lactose intolerant.

4	cups	water	2	tsp	vanilla extract
1	cup	raw cashew nuts	1/4	cup	unsweetened cocoa powder
1/4	cup	maple syrup (or agave syrup)	1/4	tsp	salt

Procedure

1 Combine all ingredients in a blender and process on high speed until well combined.

2 Store in a glass jar and refrigerate for up to 3 days.

Servings: 4

Preparation Time: 5 minutes

Nutrition Facts

Serving size: 1 cup

Cook's Notes

Amount Per Serving	
Calories	59.1
Calories From Fat (44%)	26.29
	% Daily Value
Total Fat 3.14g	5%
Saturated Fat 0.55g	3%
Cholesterol 0mg	0%
Sodium 153.49mg	6%
Potassium 52.29mg	1%
Total Carbohydrates 5.95g	2%
Fiber 0.3g	1%
Sugar 4.05g	
Protein 1.36g	3%

Coconut Oat Milk

Sounds odd but it's good.

1/2	cup	rolled oats	4	cups	water, divided
1/2	cup	pitted dates	1/2	tsp	salt
1/2	cup	unsweetened dried coconut			

Procedure

1. In a medium sauce pan combine rolled oats, dates, coconut, 1 cup of water and salt. Simmer on low heat for 15 - 20 minutes, stirring occasionally.
2. Pour warm mixture into a blender, add the remainder 3 cups of water and process until very smooth.
3. Store in a glass jar and refrigerate for up to 3 days.

Servings: 4

Preparation Time: 10 minutes

Nutrition Facts

Serving size: 1 cup

Cook's Notes

Amount Per Serving	
Calories	288.23
Calories From Fat (55%)	159.32
	% Daily Value
Total Fat 19.04g	29%
Saturated Fat 16.34g	82%
Cholesterol 0mg	0%
Sodium 309.34mg	13%
Potassium 338.98mg	10%
Total Carbohydrates 30.25g	10%
Fiber 7.42g	30%
Sugar 16.28g	
Protein 3.83g	8%

Rich Cashew Milk

I love using cashews because they're such a soft nut that they make very smooth nut milk.

1 cup	raw cashew nuts	1 Tbs maple syrup (or agave nectar)
3 cups	water	

Procedure

1 Combine all ingredients in a blender and process on high speed until well combined.

2 Store in a glass jar and refrigerate for up to 3 days.

Servings: 4

Preparation Time: 5 minutes

Nutrition Facts

Serving size: 1 cup

Cook's Notes

Amount Per Serving	
Calories	52.19
Calories From Fat (50%)	26.03
	% Daily Value
Total Fat 3.11g	5%
Saturated Fat 0.55g	3%
Cholesterol 0mg	0%
Sodium 6.78mg	<1%
Potassium 59.16mg	2%
Total Carbohydrates 5.49g	2%
Fiber 0.23g	<1%
Sugar 3.44g	
Protein 1.29g	3%

A ngel hair has always been my husband's favorite. Before his cancer, I used whole grain pasta however in the beginning, semolina pasta was much easier for him to swallow. I still use whole grain pasta but cook it longer, use short to medium size and make sure the sauce is fully absorbed to soften it. Orzo is lovely because it's just slightly larger than rice and goes down easily.

These tasty entrees can be served to family and friends and no one will know who has difficulty swallowing.

Orzo with Ground Pork (page 108)

Macaroni & Cottage Cheese (page 106)

Angel Hair in Pink Sauce

I like to use the De Boles brand Spaghetti Style Pasta made with Rice, Quinoa and Amaranth - available in most grocery stores.

4	oz	angel hair pasta (multi-grain, gluten-free)	1/2	cup	frozen baby peas, thawed and drained
4		whole canned tomatoes	1/3	cup	diced roasted red peppers
2	Tbs	heavy (whipping) cream	1	tsp	dried basil
1/2	Tbs	olive oil	2	Tbs	grated Parmesan cheese
1		garlic clove, minced			

Procedure

1 Prepare pasta according to package directions, or until very tender.

2 Place tomatoes and cream in a blender or food processor and blend until very smooth, about 1 minute. Set aside.

3 In a large skillet, heat olive oil over medium heat. Add garlic and sauté for 30 seconds. Add the peas, roasted red peppers and basil and stir 1 minute. Add the puréed tomato mixture and heat just to boiling. Remove sauce from heat.

4 Drain pasta, (reserving 1/2 cup or so of pasta cooking water), transfer to skillet, adding pasta water to thin sauce as needed. Stir over medium heat until pasta is well coated with sauce. Divide pasta between two serving bowls. Sprinkle with grated Parmesan cheese and serve immediately.

Servings: 2

Nutrition Facts

Serving size: about 1 cup

Cook's Notes

Amount Per Serving	
Calories	491.09
Calories From Fat (23%)	114.6
	% Daily Value
Total Fat 13.19g	20%
Saturated Fat 4.96g	25%
Cholesterol 24.78mg	8%
Sodium 1436.77mg	60%
Potassium 1828.15mg	52%
Total Carbohydrates 89.37g	30%
Fiber 14.25g	57%
Sugar 23.35g	
Protein 16.46g	33%

Fusilli with Cannellini Beans ⅓

I like to use the 365™ brand from Whole Foods Market but any medium pasta will work.

4 cups	whole wheat fusilli pasta or other medium pasta, uncooked	1	(16-oz) can cannellini beans, drained and rinsed
2 cups	chunky, mild salsa (your favorite)	3	Tbs chopped fresh parsley
			Salt and pepper to taste
1 Tbs	Worcestershire sauce	4	Tbs shredded Parmigiano-Reggiano cheese

Procedure

1 Prepare pasta according to package directions, plus a few minutes until pasta is soft. Drain, reserving 1/2 cup pasta water, and set aside.

2 Meanwhile in a large saucepan, stir together remaining ingredients, except parsley and cheese and heat gently on low heat, about 10 minutes.

3 Add pasta to sauce and stir gently adding pasta water as needed. Spoon onto serving plates and garnish with chopped parsley and cheese.

Servings: 4

Preparation Time: 30 minutes
Cooking Time: 15 minutes

Nutrition Facts

Serving size: about 1 cup

Cook's Notes

Amount Per Serving	
Calories	712.87
Calories From Fat (5%)	33.94
	% Daily Value
Total Fat 3.89g	6%
Saturated Fat 1.2g	6%
Cholesterol 4.4mg	1%
Sodium 538.24mg	22%
Potassium 3099.63mg	89%
Total Carbohydrates 133.44g	44%
Fiber 27.83g	111%
Sugar 7.89g	
Protein 42.23g	84%

A classic Jewish dish from Eastern Europe and Russia, made with bow-tie pasta and buckwheat groats called Kasha. It has a lovely earthy flavor with a creamy mushroom sauce.

3 1/2	cups	water	1 medium		garlic clove, minced
1/2	cup	buckwheat groats	8 oz		crimini (or button) mushrooms, thinly sliced
1/2	tsp	salt	2 tsp		fresh, chopped thyme leaves
1 1/2	cups	dry bowtie pasta	3 Tbs		all-purpose flour
2	Tbs	olive oil	2 Tbs		tamari soy sauce
1	medium	sweet onion, finely chopped	Freshly ground black pepper		

Procedure

1. In a small saucepan, bring 1 cup of the water to a boil, add groats and salt, cover and simmer over low heat until water is absorbed, about 10 minutes. Stir to fluff, cover and set aside.
2. Cook bowties in salted boiling water according to package directions adding 2 - 3 minutes extra for soft pasta. Reserve 1/2 cup liquid, drain, cover and set aside.
3. Meanwhile, in a medium skillet, heat olive oil. Add onions, garlic, mushrooms, thyme and cook over medium high heat, stirring until onions and mushrooms are soft, about 5 minutes.
4. Sprinkle in flour and stir to combine, cooking for 2 - 3 minutes.
5. Add tamari into remaining 2 1/2 cups water and whisk into skillet with mushroom mixture stirring constantly over medium heat until sauce thickens. Season with salt and pepper to taste and gently simmer for about 3 more minutes.
6. Reheat the kasha with some of the reserved cooking water to loosen. Stir kasha into bow ties, toss to combine.
7. Spoon into serving bowls topping with mushroom sauce and serve.

Servings: 4

Preparation Time: 30 minutes
Cooking Time: 15 minutes

Nutrition Facts

Serving size: about 1 ¼ cups

Cook's Notes

Amount Per Serving	
Calories	349.13
Calories From Fat (21%)	72.44
	% Daily Value
Total Fat 8.22g	13%
Saturated Fat 1.2g	6%
Cholesterol 0mg	0%
Sodium 815.16mg	34%
Potassium 850.91mg	24%
Total Carbohydrates 59.2g	20%
Fiber 4.89g	20%
Sugar 3.83g	
Protein 13g	26%

This meat-based sauce for pasta originated from Bologna, Italy. It is often referred to simply as tomato sauce with meat.

1 Tbs	extra-virgin olive oil or vegetable oil		1	cup	cottage cheese
1 lb	ground turkey		1/4	cup	tomato paste
8 oz	Italian-style turkey sausage		2 (14.5 oz)		cans diced tomatoes, drained
1/2	cup	chopped onion	1	tsp	dried basil, crushed
1/2	cup	diced carrots	1	tsp	oregano leaves, crushed
1/2	cup	diced celery	Salt to taste		
1 Tbs	minced garlic		1/2	cup	Neufchatel, (or cream cheese)
1 cup	red wine		1	cup	finely chopped fresh parsley
2	Tbs	balsamic vinegar			

Procedure

1 Heat oil in a large sauté pan over medium-high heat. Add ground turkey and sausage breaking into small chunks and cook until browned, about 8 minutes.

2 Process onion, carrot, celery and garlic in a food processor until minced and add to browned meat. Cook vegetables until soft, about 5 minutes. Turn up the heat to medium high, stir in red wine and balsamic vinegar. Cook for about 5 minutes to reduce the liquid.

3 Process cottage cheese in food processor until smooth and stir into meat mixture.

4 Stir in tomato paste and cook 1 minute. Add diced tomatoes, basil, oregano, and salt, reduce heat to medium-low and simmer sauce for 40-45 minutes, stirring occasionally.

5 Add neufchatel (or cream cheese), stirring until melted. Stir in parsley and serve.

Servings: 8
Preparation Time: 30 minutes   Cooking Time: 45 minutes

Nutrition Facts

Serving size: about 1 ¼ cups

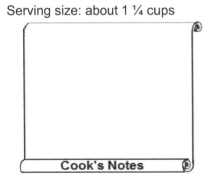

Cook's Notes

Amount Per Serving	
Calories	281
Calories From Fat (42%)	117.33
	% Daily Value
Total Fat 13.2g	20%
Saturated Fat 3.37g	17%
Cholesterol 65.91mg	22%
Sodium 554.32mg	23%
Potassium 725.27mg	21%
Total Carbohydrates 15.74g	5%
Fiber 3.38g	14%
Sugar 3.85g	
Protein 21.75g	44%

Recipe Tips

Use tomato paste which comes in a tube. It's easy to measure and can be capped for later use if stored in the refrigerator.

In Hungary this dish is called Túrós Csusza and is served after a highly seasoned fish soup named Haláuszlé. Serve the bacon on the side.

4 oz	dry elbow macaroni, medium shells or other medium pasta shape	1/2 medium	onion, chopped
		8 oz	cottage cheese, drained
2	slices bacon, cut into thin strips	4 oz	sour cream or plain yogurt
4 oz	cooked ham, cubed	Chopped parsley and paprika for serving	

Procedure

1. Cook macaroni according to package directions or until soft. Drain.
2. In a large size skillet, cook bacon pieces until crisp. Remove to paper towel and set aside.
3. In a small food processor, pulse ham until finely minced scraping down the sides if necessary. Set aside.
4. Sauté onions in bacon fat until just golden. Add drained macaroni, ham, cottage cheese and sour cream (or yogurt). Stir and warm everything by simmering on low heat for about 5 minutes.
5. Divide mixture between serving plates, sprinkle with chopped parsley, dust top with Hungarian paprika and serve passing the bacon bits separately.

Servings: 4

Preparation Time: 30 minutes
Cooking Time: 15 minutes

Nutrition Facts

Serving size: about 1 cup

Cook's Notes

Amount Per Serving	
Calories	301.07
Calories From Fat (37%)	111.57
	% Daily Value
Total Fat 12.4g	19%
Saturated Fat 4.3g	22%
Cholesterol 35.45mg	12%
Sodium 643.85mg	27%
Potassium 326.09mg	9%
Total Carbohydrates 26.13g	9%
Fiber 1.16g	5%
Sugar 5.73g	
Protein 20.07g	40%

As an alternative, try using goat cheese in place of the Boursin.

1 1/2	cups	dry shells, macaroni, or other short pasta	2	Tbs	plain Greek-style yogurt
1	large	clove garlic, peeled	2	cups	baby spinach (packed)
3	Tbs	Boursin cheese, room temperature	4	large	basil leaves, torn

Salt and freshly ground black pepper to taste

Procedure

1 Cook pasta according to package instructions plus a few minutes to make it soft. Reserve ½ cup of cooking liquid.

2 While pasta cooks, in the bowl of a food processor while motor is running, drop in garlic clove and process until chopped.

3 Add Boursin cheese, yogurt, spinach and basil leaves. Season with salt and pepper and process to a smooth consistency.

4 Scrape into a large serving bowl. Add cooked pasta and reserved cooking water, toss to combine, and season with additional salt and pepper to taste.

Servings: 2

Preparation Time: 15 minutes

Nutrition Facts

Serving size: about 1 cup

Cook's Notes

Amount Per Serving	
Calories	482.26
Calories From Fat (35%)	169.5
	% Daily Value
Total Fat 20.05g	31%
Saturated Fat 13.11g	66%
Cholesterol 50.53mg	17%
Sodium 323.9mg	13%
Potassium 352.46mg	10%
Total Carbohydrates 62.89g	21%
Fiber 2.67g	11%
Sugar 1.23g	
Protein 14.82g	30%

Recipe Tips

Use semolina pasta, whole wheat or De Boles' artichoke pasta.
Serve as a main course or as a side dish for 4 portions.

I love using orzo whole wheat pasta. It's shaped like rice only it's slightly bigger, and the whole wheat adds more fiber.

1/4	cup	orzo, or other small pasta shape, uncooked	1/2	tsp	minced garlic
			1/2	tsp	salt
1	Tbs	olive oil	1	tsp	Italian seasoning
1	cup	chopped mushrooms	1/4	lb.	ground pork
1/4	cup	chopped onion	1 (14 oz can) diced tomatoes		
			Parmesan cheese for serving		

Procedure

1 In a small saucepan, cook orzo according to package instructions plus 2 - 3 minutes or until soft.

2 In a medium-size skillet, heat olive oil on medium high heat and sauté mushrooms until slightly brown, about 5 minutes.

3 Add onions and garlic, sprinkle in the salt and Italian seasoning and continue to cook for another few minutes until the onions soften.

4 Crumble in ground pork (or use a potato masher) and cook until pork is no longer pink, about 8 minutes.

5 Add the tomatoes and stir to combine. Drain orzo and add to skillet. Stir and gently simmer for a few minutes to allow orzo to soak a little of the tomato liquid.

6 Serve with a sprinkle of Parmesan cheese.

Servings: 2

Preparation Time: 25 minutes

Nutrition Facts

Serving size: about 1 cup

Cook's Notes

Amount Per Serving	
Calories	275.08
Calories From Fat (63%)	171.93
	% Daily Value
Total Fat 19.25g	30%
Saturated Fat 5.47g	27%
Cholesterol 40.82mg	14%
Sodium 629.39mg	26%
Potassium 588.48mg	17%
Total Carbohydrates 14.16g	5%
Fiber 2.13g	9%
Sugar 4.66g	
Protein 13.34g	27%

Here the mushroom takes the place of meat.

1/4	cup	orzo pasta (whole wheat), uncooked
1	Tbs	unsalted butter
1	Tbs	olive oil
1	large	Portobello mushroom cap, finely chopped
1/2	cup	finely chopped sweet onion
1/2	tsp	minced garlic

1	tsp	dried basil
1/2	tsp	Italian seasoning
Salt and pepper to taste		
3	Tbs	sun-dried tomatoes, drained and cut into strips
1	cup	baby spinach (about 2 handfuls)
1	Tbs	grated Parmigiano-Reggiano cheese

Procedure

1. In a small saucepan, cook orzo according to package instructions, plus 2 -3 minutes for soft pasta. Reserve 1/2 cup cooking liquid, drain, cover and set aside.
2. While pasta cooks, in a medium-size skillet, melt butter and olive oil over medium high heat. Add the onions and sauté until soft, about 5 minutes. Add garlic and stir.
3. Add mushrooms stirring to combine. Crumble in basil and Italian seasoning, season with salt and pepper and cook until mushrooms are tender, 8 - 10 minutes. Sprinkle in sun-dried tomatoes and cook another few minutes, stirring often.
4. Add pasta and just enough pasta cooking water to moisten everything.
5. Add spinach, toss until it wilts, and add more pasta water if necessary.
6. Once spinach wilts, pour mixture onto a serving plate, top with cheese and serve.

Servings: 1

Preparation Time: 15 minutes
Cooking Time: 25 minutes

Nutrition Facts

Serving size: about 1 cup

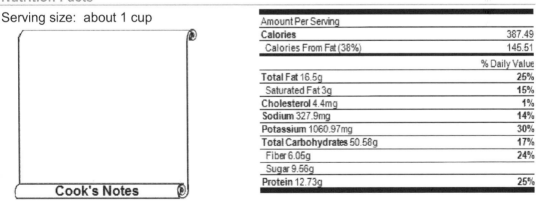

Cook's Notes

Amount Per Serving	
Calories	387.49
Calories From Fat (38%)	145.51
	% Daily Value
Total Fat 16.5g	25%
Saturated Fat 3g	15%
Cholesterol 4.4mg	1%
Sodium 327.9mg	14%
Potassium 1060.97mg	30%
Total Carbohydrates 50.58g	17%
Fiber 6.05g	24%
Sugar 9.56g	
Protein 12.73g	25%

Recipe Tips

As an alternative, use 1 cup of frozen peas in place of the spinach.

As long as I include things like artichoke hearts, tomatoes and other moist vegetables, we are able to enjoy salads. I use plain yogurt, mayonnaise and lemon flavored flax oil and a lot of fresh herbs. The egg salad is one of our staples, especially when we travel on an airplane.

Composed Salad (page 116)

Pickled Beet Tzatziki Salad (page 119)

Arame (Seaweed) Salad

This is a great pairing with Salmon. Even if you think you don't like seaweed, try it, you'll love it!

For the Salad

2	cups	arame seaweed, (preferably Eden brand)
1	cup	sliced baby carrots
1/2	cup	sliced roasted red peppers
1/2	cup	grated radish
4		scallions, thinly sliced
2	tsp	olive oil

2 garlic cloves, minced
1 Tbs fresh ginger root, peeled and minced

For the Dressing

3 Tbs rice vinegar, seasoned
2 Tbs tamari soy sauce
2 Tbs sesame oil, dark
2 Tbs sesame seeds for garnish (optional)

Procedure

1. Place seaweed in a glass bowl and add hot water to cover. Set aside to soak for 15 minutes. Drain and place in a medium-size saucepan.
2. Add carrots to saucepan with arame and add just enough water to barely cover. Cover and bring to a boil over high heat. Reduce heat to low, simmer until carrots are tender, about 5 minutes. Drain and transfer to a large bowl.
3. Add red peppers, radishes and scallions.
4. In a small nonstick skillet, heat olive oil over medium heat and sauté garlic and ginger until fragrant, about 2 minutes. Add to the arame mixture.
5. Make dressing by combining vinegar, tamari and sesame oil in a jar with a tight-fitting lid. Shake dressing vigorously and pour over the arame salad, tossing to combine. Sprinkle with sesame seeds, (if using). Serve immediately or chill for 30 minutes.

Servings: 4

Preparation Time: 30 minutes
Cooking Time: 10 minutes

Nutrition Facts

Serving size: a generous cupful

Cook's Notes

Amount Per Serving	
Calories	166.84
Calories From Fat (22%)	37.32
	% Daily Value
Total Fat 11.38g	18%
Saturated Fat 1.61g	8%
Cholesterol 0mg	0%
Sodium 588.85mg	25%
Potassium 1536.11mg	44%
Total Carbohydrates 84.42g	28%
Fiber 5.2g	21%
Sugar 1.08g	
Protein 2.88g	6%

Asparagus Pyramid Salad

Inspired by Ingrid Hoffmann, this salad is beautiful, has lots of fiber and is scrumptious. The sherry vinegar and agave syrup adds just the right blend of sweet and tart.

For the Vinaigrette
2	Tbs	sherry vinegar
1/2	tsp	agave syrup
Salt and black pepper, to taste		
1	Tbs	chopped fresh tarragon
1/4	cup	extra-virgin olive oil

For the Salad
10		asparagus spears, trimmed
1/2	lb	fresh green beans, trimmed and cut in 2-3" lengths
1	cup	freshly grated carrots
1/2	cup	canned black beans, drained and rinsed

Procedure

1. Make vinaigrette by combining all ingredients in a glass jar with a tight-fitting lid. Shake vigorously to emulsify dressing. Set aside.
2. In a large pot of boiling, salted water, blanch asparagus 3 - 5 minutes until crisp-tender. Scoop into an ice bath with a strainer to cool.
3. Blanch green beans in the same cooking water 5 - 7 minutes. Scoop into ice bath with asparagus to cool completely, drain and dry with paper towels. Pick out asparagus spears and set aside.
4. In a medium-size bowl, combine carrots, black beans and green beans. Toss with a little dressing to coat vegetables.
5. Arrange a small mound in the center of 2 salad plates. Lean 5 asparagus spears against each other joining the tips in the center.
6. Drizzle with remaining dressing and serve.

Servings: 2

Preparation Time: 10 minutes
Cooking Time: 10 minutes

Nutrition Facts

Serving size: 2 pyramids

Cook's Notes

Amount Per Serving	
Calories	428.74
Calories From Fat (57%)	245.8
	% Daily Value
Total Fat 27.95g	43%
Saturated Fat 3.95g	20%
Cholesterol 0mg	0%
Sodium 47.93mg	2%
Potassium 893.68mg	26%
Total Carbohydrates 37.72g	13%
Fiber 13.66g	55%
Sugar 7.99g	
Protein 11.9g	24%

Avocado Papaya Salad

This is a very colorful and flavorful salad, especially in the summer.

1	medium	avocado, preferably Hass, peeled and cut into 1/2-inch dice	2	Tbs	extra-virgin olive oil
			2	Tbs	flax oil with lemon
			1/8	tsp	freshly ground black pepper
1	medium	papaya, peeled, seeded and cut into 1/2-inch dice	1/8	tsp	salt
1	Tbs	agave nectar			
1		lime, juiced			

Procedure

1. In a medium-size bowl combine avocado and papaya.
2. In a small bowl, whisk remaining ingredients until combined. Pour dressing over fruit, toss very gently and serve immediately.

Servings: 4

Preparation Time: 10 minutes

Nutrition Facts

Serving size: about ¾ cup

Cook's Notes

Amount Per Serving	
Calories	235.97
Calories From Fat (75%)	176.76
	% Daily Value
Total Fat 20.34g	31%
Saturated Fat 2.52g	13%
Cholesterol 0mg	0%
Sodium 79.74mg	3%
Potassium 256.69mg	7%
Total Carbohydrates 15.45g	5%
Fiber 3.8g	15%
Sugar 9.95g	
Protein 1.08g	2%

This is a wonderful combination of flavors. The Fresno chili looks much like a jalapeño but is red in color and has a much milder heat level. It is optional but if it can be tolerated adds a lovely fruity-like heat in the background.

1 (14 oz)	can artichoke hearts, drained and quartered	
1 (14 oz)	can hearts of palm, sliced	
1/2	small	red onion, thinly sliced
1	small	dill pickle, finely chopped
1	small	Fresno chili, minced (optional)
1/4	cup	coarsely chopped fresh cilantro

2 medium avocados, preferably Hass, peeled and cut into 1/2-inch dice
3 Tbs white wine vinegar
Salt and pepper to taste
8 large butter lettuce leaves to serve

Procedure

1 In a medium-size bowl, combine artichoke hearts, hearts of palm, onion, pickle, chili (if using), and cilantro. Add avocado, vinegar and season with salt and freshly ground black pepper. Mix gently to combine flavors but not break up avocados.

2 Spoon into lettuce leaves and serve chilled.

Servings: 4

Preparation Time: 15 minutes

Nutrition Facts

Serving size: 2 lettuce leaves with ½ cup filling in each

Cook's Notes

Amount Per Serving	
Calories	195.29
Calories From Fat (60%)	116.73
	% Daily Value
Total Fat 14g	22%
Saturated Fat 1.94g	10%
Cholesterol 0mg	0%
Sodium 277.22mg	12%
Potassium 1022.7mg	29%
Total Carbohydrates 17.42g	6%
Fiber 10.3g	41%
Sugar 2.06g	
Protein 5.91g	12%

Beet & Apple Salad

The beets add so much sweetness that the horseradish provides just a little tang in the background. You may want to decrease the amount though – it depends on how strong your particular brand is.

4	large	beets
5		thyme sprigs
1/2	cup	extra virgin olive oil
1/4	cup	apple cider vinegar

1 tsp	Dijon mustard
3 Tbs	prepared horseradish
Salt and pepper to taste	
1	green apple, sliced paper-thin

Procedure

1. Preheat oven to 375°.
2. In a baking dish, lightly drizzle beets and thyme with olive oil. Season with salt and pepper. Cover with foil and roast until the beets are tender about 1 hour and 45 minutes. Let cool, then peel and cut into 3/4" dice.
3. In a large bowl whisk the vinegar with the mustard. Whisk in the remaining oil until emulsified. Add horseradish, season with salt and pepper, add beets and toss to coat with dressing.
4. Transfer to a serving dish and top with the apple slices.

Servings: 8

Preparation Time: 30 minutes
Cooking Time: 2 hours and 15 minutes

Nutrition Facts

Serving size: about 1 cup

Cook's Notes

Amount Per Serving	
Calories	161.95
Calories From Fat (75%)	121.16
	% Daily Value
Total Fat 13.72g	21%
Saturated Fat 1.9g	10%
Cholesterol 0mg	0%
Sodium 79.37mg	3%
Potassium 261mg	7%
Total Carbohydrates 9.53g	3%
Fiber 2.55g	10%
Sugar 6.7g	
Protein 1.26g	3%

Composed Salad ⅓

This makes an ideal summer lunch. Use the upper third of the avocado either chopped in the salad or in a smoothie.

1 cup	shredded romaine lettuce leaves	5	Kalamata olives, sliced in half lengthwise
1 slice	tomato, preferably heirloom (1/4" thick)	1/2	avocado, preferably Hass
2 - 3	artichoke hearts, drained & quartered	1	scoop egg salad (page 117)
1/4 small	sweet onion, thinly sliced	1/2	oz smoked salmon, cut into small pieces
5	tomatoes, cherry or grape, sliced in half lengthwise	Drizzle of salad Dressing of choice to serve	

Procedure

1 Scatter shredded lettuce on a serving plate and place sliced tomato in center. Arrange artichoke hearts, sliced onions, tomatoes and olives all around. Set aside.

2 Cut top 1/3 of avocado around the seed. Twist to separate, remove pit and discard. Cut a small piece off the bottom so it will stand upright creating a bowl. Gently peel the bottom half and place on top of tomato slice.

3 Using an ice cream scoop (or spoon) fill avocado cavity with egg salad mound.

4 Scatter smoked salmon on top and around avocado. Drizzle with dressing (or use a squeeze bottle and dress in a cross-hatch pattern) and serve.

Servings: 1

Preparation Time: 10 minutes

Nutrition Facts

Cook's Notes

Amount Per Serving	
Calories	283.83
Calories From Fat (58%)	165.59
	% Daily Value
Total Fat 19.35g	30%
Saturated Fat 2g	10%
Cholesterol 3.26mg	1%
Sodium 678.8mg	28%
Potassium 1031.37mg	29%
Total Carbohydrates 24.94g	8%
Fiber 12.28g	49%
Sugar 1.76g	
Protein 8.48g	17%

Egg Salad

Use more yogurt and less mayonnaise if you prefer a tangier taste.

4	large	eggs, hard boiled, peeled
1/4	cup	scallions, thinly sliced (white part and tips of green part)
1/4	cup	mayonnaise
2	Tbs	plain Greek-style yogurt
1/2	tsp	Dijon mustard (more if desired)

1/4	tsp	salt
1/4	tsp	black pepper
1/4	tsp	turmeric (optional)
1/2	tsp	curry powder (optional)

Procedure

1 In a medium-size bowl grate hard-boiled eggs and add all other ingredients, stirring to combine.

2 Taste and adjust salt and pepper and add more mustard if desired.

Servings: 4

Preparation Time: 15 minutes
Cooking Time: 15 minutes
Inactive Time: 12 minutes

Nutrition Facts

Serving size: about 1/3 cup

Cook's Notes

Amount Per Serving	
Calories	144.76
Calories From Fat (64%)	93.08
	% Daily Value
Total Fat 10.42g	16%
Saturated Fat 2.45g	12%
Cholesterol 190.78mg	64%
Sodium 325.47mg	14%
Potassium 103.31mg	3%
Total Carbohydrates 5.68g	2%
Fiber 0.29g	1%
Sugar 2.38g	
Protein 6.99g	14%

This recipe comes from my friend Regina's late husband Vadim. He was a Russian émigré and had a passion for cooking, especially traditional Russian dishes. I don't know if this is Russian but according to Regina, it is always a hit when served to guests.

4	small	red potatoes, quartered	1/3	cup	sliced roasted red peppers
1	cup	cauliflower florets		**For the Dressing**	
1	cup	baby carrots, sliced thick	3/4	cup	mayonnaise
1	cup	frozen baby peas	1	Tbs	apple cider vinegar
1		Granny Smith or Macintosh apple, cored, peeled and chopped	1/4	cup	sweet pickle relish
			1/2	Tbs	Dijon mustard
			1/2	tsp	chopped fresh dill sprigs
1	small	sweet onion, thinly sliced	1/2	tsp	salt
1	small	zucchini or yellow squash, halved lengthwise and cut crosswise into 1/2" pieces	1/2	Tbs	sugar or equivalent sweetener
			1/4	tsp	freshly ground black pepper

Procedure

1 In a large pot cover potatoes with water by 2 inches, bring to a boil, toss in carrots and cauliflower and boil until vegetables are tender. Add frozen peas during the last 5 minutes.

2 Drain vegetables, rinse with cold water to stop the cooking process and place in a large mixing bowl, allowing to cool completely.

3 In a small bowl, combine the apple, onions, zucchini and peppers. Mix to combine. Add to vegetables and toss gently.

To make Dressing

4 To make dressing combine all ingredients in a medium-size bowl, beating well.

5 Pour dressing over vegetables and fold to coat evenly. Set aside for 2 to 3 hours and allow salad to develop its flavor before serving at room temperature.

Servings: 8

Preparation Time: 30 minutes

Nutrition Facts

Serving size: 1 1/4 cups (about 6 oz.)

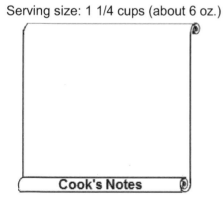

Cook's Notes

Amount Per Serving	
Calories	181.96
Calories From Fat (37%)	66.61
	% Daily Value
Total Fat 7.64g	12%
Saturated Fat 1.13g	6%
Cholesterol 5.73mg	2%
Sodium 365.13mg	15%
Potassium 527.7mg	15%
Total Carbohydrates 27.13g	9%
Fiber 2.88g	12%
Sugar 5.71g	
Protein 3.19g	6%

Pickled Beet Tzatziki Salad

Tzatziki, is a Greek appetizer also used as a sauce for souvlaki and gyros. It is made of strained yoghurt from sheep or goat milk, usually mixed with cucumbers, garlic, salt, olive oil and pepper. Sometimes lemon juice and parsley are added with dill or mint as well. It is always served cold. The pickled beets in this version give it a lovely color.

8	oz	plain Greek-style yogurt	2 scallions, thinly sliced (white part and tips of green part)
1/2	cup	pickled beets, grated	
4	oz	feta cheese, crumbled	Salt and freshly ground black pepper to taste

Procedure

1 In a medium bowl mix all ingredients together and taste for seasoning. Pour into a serving bowl.

2 Serve chilled as a side dish or salad.

Servings: 6

Preparation Time: 5 minutes

Nutrition Facts

Serving size: ½ cup

Cook's Notes

Amount Per Serving	
Calories	100.08
Calories From Fat (41%)	41.03
	% Daily Value
Total Fat 4.65g	7%
Saturated Fat 3.21g	16%
Cholesterol 19.13mg	6%
Sodium 338.17mg	14%
Potassium 170.46mg	5%
Total Carbohydrates 9.98g	3%
Fiber 1.12g	4%
Sugar 6.04g	
Protein 5.07g	10%

Sauces are a great way to facilitate the swallowing process. Marinades are used to help break down the fiber of proteins to make them softer. However be aware that sauces and marinades only go so far. Food still has to have internal moisture to be swallowed easily.

Veracruz Sauce (page 131) & Celeriac Mash (page 151) with Baked Sea Bass & Broccoli

White Sauce (page 132) & Kauli Pilaf (page 156) with Grilled Salmon

Cheddar Cheese Sauce (page 124)

Anchovy Sauce

This sauce pairs well with grilled steak or meaty fish like tuna. Don't let the anchovy paste scare you - it won't taste fishy at all! The flavor is thick, rich and silky.

1 medium	garlic clove		6	Tbs	heavy (whipping) cream
1 Tbs	roughly chopped fresh tarragon		1 1/2	Tbs	anchovy paste
4	shallots, peeled and quartered				
2 Tbs	unsalted butter				

Procedure

1. In a small food processor drop in the garlic clove and mince. Add the tarragon and pulse several times to finely chop. Add the shallots and pulse to a fine chop.
2. In a small skillet or saucepan heat the butter on medium heat until melted, add the onion mixture from the food processor and sauté until shallots are tender, about 5 minutes.
3. Add cream and anchovy paste and heat gently stirring until mixture thickens, 4 - 5 minutes. Do not allow sauce to boil.

Servings: 2

Preparation Time: 10 minutes
Cooking Time: 10 minutes

Nutrition Facts

Serving size: about 3 Tablespoons

Cook's Notes

Amount Per Serving	
Calories	302.39
Calories From Fat (85%)	257.06
	% Daily Value
Total Fat 29.23g	45%
Saturated Fat 18.17g	91%
Cholesterol 86.62mg	29%
Sodium 234.44mg	10%
Potassium 208.96mg	6%
Total Carbohydrates 8.32g	3%
Fiber 0.06g	<1%
Sugar 0.06g	
Protein 3.56g	7%

BBQ Sauce

This version adapted from Rachael Ray is excellent. Use it as a basting sauce when grilling, as a dipping sauce or on an open-faced sandwich.

1 cup ketchup, organic		2 Tbs	Worcestershire sauce
2 Tbs Dijon mustard		1 tsp	black pepper
2 Tbs dark brown sugar (or palm sugar)		1 Tbs	bourbon or whiskey (optional)
2 Tbs maple syrup (or agave syrup)		2 large	garlic cloves, minced
2 Tbs apple cider vinegar			Juice of half an orange

Procedure

1 Combine all ingredients in a small pot and simmer over medium-low heat, stirring occasionally, for 20 minutes. Store in a glass container for up to 1 week.

Servings: 8

Preparation Time: 10 minutes
Cooking Time: 20 minutes

Nutrition Facts

Serving size: ¼ cup

Cook's Notes

Amount Per Serving	
Calories	70.31
Calories From Fat (3%)	2.33
	% Daily Value
Total Fat 0.28g	<1%
Saturated Fat 0.03g	<1%
Cholesterol 0mg	0%
Sodium 424.8mg	18%
Potassium 188.65mg	5%
Total Carbohydrates 16.35g	5%
Fiber 0.28g	1%
Sugar 14.09g	
Protein 0.82g	2%

Blender Hollandaise

The cayenne pepper, which is usually one of the ingredients, is omitted here. You can add a tiny amount of Dijon mustard and a small dash of white pepper if it can be tolerated.

1/2	cup	salted butter	1/8	tsp	Dijon mustard
2	large	egg yolks	Dash of white pepper		
2	tsp	fresh lemon juice	1	Tbs	hot water

Procedure

1. In a small saucepan melt butter until almost bubbling. Rinse a small blender jar with hot water.
2. Place egg yolks, lemon juice, mustard, and white pepper into blender jar, blend on medium speed for a couple of seconds.
3. Remove center section of blender cap and while motor is running, pour melted butter in very slowly, tiny drops at first until it starts to thicken, and then in a slow, steady stream until mixture is very thick. Add the hot water a little at a time until it reaches desired consistency.

Servings: 4

Preparation Time: 5 minutes
Cooking Time: 5 minutes

Nutrition Facts

Serving size: about 2 to 3 Tablespoons

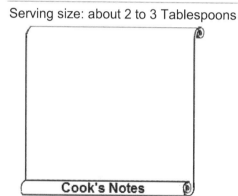

Cook's Notes

Amount Per Serving	
Calories	231.53
Calories From Fat (96%)	222.63
	% Daily Value
Total Fat 25.26g	39%
Saturated Fat 15.37g	77%
Cholesterol 153.17mg	51%
Sodium 9.21mg	<1%
Potassium 17.72mg	<1%
Total Carbohydrates 0.54g	<1%
Fiber 0.05g	<1%
Sugar 0.1g	
Protein 1.62g	3%

Recipe Tips

By pouring melted butter into a measuring cup with a spout you will have more control pouring into the blender.

Serve over steamed asparagus, other vegetables and of course poached eggs.

Cheddar Cheese Sauce

Delicious on baked potatoes, vegetables or try it on my Tostada Hay Stacks (page 93).

1	cup	almond milk (organic, unsweetened)
1 1/2	Tbs	cornstarch (or arrowroot)
1/4	tsp	dry mustard (Coleman's brand)
1/4	tsp	salt
1	Tbs	chopped pimientos
3/4	cup	grated sharp white cheddar cheese

Procedure

1 Combine all ingredients, (except cheese) in a small blender and process until smooth.

2 Pour into a small saucepan and bring to a simmer on medium heat, stirring until thickened. Add the cheese in stages, and stir until melted.

Servings: 6
Yield: 1 1/2 cups

Nutrition Facts

Serving size: ¼ cup

Cook's Notes

Amount Per Serving	
Calories	66.55
Calories From Fat (62%)	41.51
	% Daily Value
Total Fat 4.72g	7%
Saturated Fat 2.98g	15%
Cholesterol 14.83mg	5%
Sodium 187.03mg	8%
Potassium 26.76mg	<1%
Total Carbohydrates 2.4g	<1%
Fiber 0.02g	<1%
Sugar 0.07g	
Protein 3.62g	7%

Curried Sesame Sauce

Easy and delicious over steamed vegetables or baked potatoes. To create a milder flavor stir in a little plain yogurt or heavy cream.

1	cup	water	1 Tbs curry powder
2/3	cup	tahini (sesame paste)	2 Tbs Tamari soy sauce (gluten-free)

Procedure

1 Measure all ingredients directly into a small blender and purée until smooth. Pour into a small saucepan and simmer gently, stirring constantly until mixture thickens.

2 Remove from the heat, cover and allow flavors to blend. Taste, adjust seasoning and serve.

Servings: 4

Preparation Time: 5 minutes
Cooking Time: 10 minutes

Nutrition Facts

Serving size: ¼ cup

Cook's Notes

Amount Per Serving	
Calories	238.59
Calories From Fat (68%)	162.61
	% Daily Value
Total Fat 19.43g	30%
Saturated Fat 2.73g	14%
Cholesterol 0mg	0%
Sodium 534.95mg	22%
Potassium 209.63mg	6%
Total Carbohydrates 11.9g	4%
Fiber 4.32g	17%
Sugar 0.2g	
Protein 8.27g	17%

Recipe Tips

Tamari soy sauce is generally gluten free, but be sure to check the label.

It's wonderful on grilled baby lamb chops but equally wonderful on fish.

2	Tbs	white wine vinegar
1/2	tsp	honey
1/2	tsp	minced garlic
1/4	cup	extra-virgin olive oil

1/3	cup	packed fresh mint leaves, finely chopped
1	medium	plum tomato, seeded and finely chopped

Salt and freshly ground black pepper to taste

Procedure

1 In a medium-size jar with a tight fitting lid, measure and combine all ingredients. Secure lid and shake vigorously until emulsified.

2 Refrigerate for at least an hour to combine flavors. Shake jar again before serving.

Servings: 4

Preparation Time: 10 minutes

Nutrition Facts

Serving size: about 2 to 3 Tablespoons

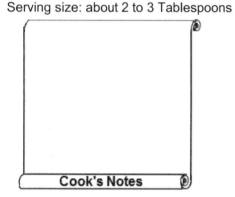

Cook's Notes

Amount Per Serving	
Calories	133.25
Calories From Fat (90%)	119.65
	% Daily Value
Total Fat 13.61g	21%
Saturated Fat 1.88g	9%
Cholesterol 0mg	0%
Sodium 3.38mg	<1%
Potassium 129.46mg	4%
Total Carbohydrates 3.37g	1%
Fiber 0.73g	3%
Sugar 1.92g	
Protein 0.51g	1%

It is outstanding on cooked vegetables.

2 Tbs peanut butter
2 Tbs maple syrup (or agave syrup)
2 Tbs Tamari soy sauce

1/4 cup water
1 Tbs fresh squeezed orange juice

Procedure

1 Combine and stir all ingredients in a glass jar with a tight-fitting lid and shake until sauce is smooth, or blend in a small blender.

Servings: 4
Yield: 1/2 cup

Preparation Time: 5 minutes

Nutrition Facts

Serving size: 2 Tablespoons

Cook's Notes

Amount Per Serving	
Calories	107.52
Calories From Fat (63%)	67.57
	% Daily Value
Total Fat 8.08g	12%
Saturated Fat 1.65g	8%
Cholesterol 0mg	0%
Sodium 505.94mg	21%
Potassium 130.82mg	4%
Total Carbohydrates 5.71g	2%
Fiber 1.04g	4%
Sugar 3.63g	
Protein 4.99g	10%

Recipe Tips

Cashew butter or almond butter may be used instead of peanut butter.

Paprika Sauce

My Hungarian ancestors may be rolling in their collective graves for using peppers and tomatoes from a jar and a can but when one has difficulty swallowing, this seems to work better than fresh. The taste is excellent and the addition of smoked paprika gives it a little extra zip! Serve it over cooked fish, pasta, or other protein.

1	Tbs	unsalted butter		1/2	Tbs	paprika (Hungarian sweet)
1/2	Tbs	olive oil		1/2	Tbs	paprika, smoked
1	large	onion, chopped		1/2		(14.5 oz) can diced tomatoes, drained, liquid reserved
1/2	tsp	crushed garlic (optional)				
1	cup	roasted red peppers		1/2	tsp	salt
				1/4	tsp	freshly ground black pepper
				1/4	cup	sour cream or plain yogurt

Procedure

1. In a large skillet heat the butter and olive oil on medium heat, add onions and sauté until slightly brown, for 8 minutes. Add garlic if using and mix to combine.
2. Add peppers and continue to sauté for about 5 minutes, stirring often.
3. Slide skillet from the heat and sprinkle in the sweet and smoked paprika. (It creates a bitter taste if burned).
4. Once paprika is incorporated, add tomatoes and return to the heat. Season with salt and pepper, cover and simmer on very low heat for about 20 minutes. Stir occasionally adding bits of reserved tomato juice to keep things moist.
5. Stir in the sour cream, taste and adjust seasoning and pour mixture into a food processor fitted with a metal blade. Process to a fairly smooth consistency scraping down the sides as necessary.
6. Serve over cooked fish or pasta.

Servings: 4
Preparation Time: 15 minutes
Cooking Time: 20 minutes

Nutrition Facts

Serving size: about 1/3 cup

Cook's Notes

Amount Per Serving	
Calories	74.17
Calories From Fat (59%)	43.9
	% Daily Value
Total Fat 5g	8%
Saturated Fat 2.25g	11%
Cholesterol 8.55mg	3%
Sodium 304.43mg	13%
Potassium 152.76mg	4%
Total Carbohydrates 6.65g	2%
Fiber 1.47g	6%
Sugar 2.76g	
Protein 1.8g	3%

I love using fresh cilantro. This is a lovely marinade.

1/4	cup	chopped fresh cilantro	1 Tbs	peeled and minced fresh ginger
1		scallion, cut into 1-inch slices	1 Tbs	fresh lime juice
1	Tbs	olive oil	1 tsp	toasted sesame oil
1	Tbs	tamari soy sauce		

Procedure

1 Puree all ingredients in a small food processor. Transfer to a bowl and marinate seafood for 10 minutes.

Servings: 4

Preparation Time: 15 minutes

Nutrition Facts

Serving size: about 1 Tablespoon

Cook's Notes

Amount Per Serving	
Calories	52.75
Calories From Fat (77%)	40.42
	% Daily Value
Total Fat 4.58g	7%
Saturated Fat 0.64g	3%
Cholesterol 0mg	0%
Sodium 139.21mg	6%
Potassium 101.62mg	3%
Total Carbohydrates 2.89g	<1%
Fiber 0.81g	3%
Sugar 0.74g	
Protein 0.77g	2%

Tahini Yogurt Sauce

Best served at room temperature to bring out all the flavors and is terrific on grilled salmon. This inspiration comes from the grilling guru Steven Raichlen.

3	Tbs	plain Greek-style yogurt	1/2	tsp	ground cumin
3	Tbs	fresh lemon juice	2	tsp	tamari soy sauce
2	Tbs	tahini (sesame paste)			Scallion greens or chives for garnish
1/2	tsp	crushed garlic			

Procedure

1 In a small bowl, whisk all ingredients together (except garnish) and season with freshly ground pepper to taste. Sprinkle with the scallion greens before serving.

Servings: 4
Yield: 1/2 cup

Preparation Time: 5 minutes

Nutrition Facts

Serving size: about 1/2 cup

Cook's Notes

Amount Per Serving	
Calories	791.4
Calories From Fat (73%)	575.99
	% Daily Value
Total Fat 68.24g	105%
Saturated Fat 9.26g	46%
Cholesterol 1.38mg	<1%
Sodium 105.42mg	4%
Potassium 557.06mg	16%
Total Carbohydrates 33.53g	11%
Fiber 11.29g	45%
Sugar 1.63g	
Protein 22.69g	45%

Veracruz Sauce

You can cook chicken or fish right in this delicious sauce.

1	medium	onion, thinly sliced
6	cloves	garlic, thinly sliced
1	(14 oz)	can diced tomatoes, with liquid
2		bay leaves
1	tsp	oregano leaves, crushed (preferably Mexican)

3/4	cup	green olives (pimento-stuffed), sliced
2	Tbs	capers, drained
1	tsp	salt
		Freshly ground pepper to taste
2	Tbs	chopped fresh parsley for garnish

Procedure

1 In a large saucepan heat olive oil on medium high heat and sauté onions until caramelized, about 6 minutes. Add garlic and cook 1 minute more, stirring.

2 Add tomatoes and all other ingredients, except parsley. Cook, stirring frequently until tomatoes are soft and sauce thickens, about 15 minutes.

3 Season with salt and pepper to taste.

4 Serve topped with chopped parsley.

Servings: 4

Preparation Time: 15 minutes
Cooking Time: 20 minutes

Nutrition Facts

Serving size: about ½ cup

Cook's Notes

Amount Per Serving	
Calories	70.23
Calories From Fat (48%)	33.51
	% Daily Value
Total Fat 3.93g	6%
Saturated Fat 0.54g	3%
Cholesterol 0mg	0%
Sodium 1148.53mg	48%
Potassium 186.95mg	5%
Total Carbohydrates 8.84g	3%
Fiber 2.74g	11%
Sugar 2.46g	
Protein 1.53g	3%

131

White Sauce

I serve this sauce at dinner parties and fool everyone because no one guesses that the basic ingredient is cauliflower. The lemon-flavored flax oil gives it a hint of lemon and contributes to the richness of the sauce. Add a touch of Dijon mustard for a zippier tang.

2 cups	cauliflower florets (about 12 oz.)	1	Tbs	flax oil with lemon
3 cups	water	1/2	cup	heavy (whipping) cream
1 tsp	salt	White pepper to taste		

Procedure

1. In a large sauce pan combine cauliflower, water and salt. Bring to a boil, reduce heat and simmer until very soft, 25 - 30 minutes.
2. Remove from heat, reserve about 1/2 cup of cooking liquid, and drain.
3. Place cauliflower, flax oil and heavy cream into a food processor and purée until very smooth, adding cooking liquid to reach desired consistency. Season with salt and white pepper to taste.

Servings: 4

Preparation Time: 10 minutes
Cooking Time: 30 minutes

Nutrition Facts

Serving size: about 1 cup

Cook's Notes

Amount Per Serving	
Calories	115.14
Calories From Fat (85%)	98
	% Daily Value
Total Fat 11.15g	17%
Saturated Fat 6.88g	34%
Cholesterol 40.76mg	14%
Sodium 1194.38mg	50%
Potassium 173.83mg	5%
Total Carbohydrates 3.32g	1%
Fiber 1g	4%
Sugar 0.99g	
Protein 1.57g	3%

Recipe Tips

Excellent on grilled or broiled salmon.

This is among the easiest of the soft, easy-to-chew foods to prepare. It also provides a good source of protein without a lot of fat. There's a wide range of seafood to choose from and when combined with the variety of preparation choices it's easy to see why so many of these recipes are favorites.

Crab Stuffed Portobello Mushrooms (page 140) & Arame (Seaweed) Salad (page 111)

Fish in Parchment (page 141)

Crab and Cheese Pie (page 137)

Scallops in Thousand Island (page 144) & Kauli Pilaf (page 156)

Beaufort Cod

My sister-in-law gave me this really simple recipe. You can use other white fish such as cod or halibut too.

2 (4 oz)	cod fish fillets	1	Tbs olive oil
Salt and pepper to taste		1	(14 oz) can diced tomatoes, with
2 tsp	Italian seasoning		liquid
		Juice of 1/2 a lemon	

Procedure

1 Season both sides of fish with salt, pepper and Italian seasoning.

2 In a medium-size skillet heat olive oil on medium-high heat. Sear the fish (flesh side down) for 2 minutes and turn them over carefully with a fish spatula. Add tomatoes and their liquid and lemon juice and cook covered for 5 - 7 minutes or until fish flakes easily.

3 Season with salt and pepper to taste and serve.

Servings: 2

Preparation Time: 5 minutes
Cooking Time: 10 minutes

Nutrition Facts

Serving size: 1 cod fillet

Cook's Notes

Amount Per Serving	
Calories	169.6
Calories From Fat (39%)	66.46
	% Daily Value
Total Fat 7.54g	12%
Saturated Fat 1.06g	5%
Cholesterol 54.52mg	18%
Sodium 1304.4mg	54%
Potassium 528.72mg	15%
Total Carbohydrates 7.53g	3%
Fiber 1.49g	6%
Sugar 3.6g	
Protein 18.84g	38%

Cheesy Catfish

Just 3 ingredients but wait until you taste them!

2	catfish fillets (or other white fish fillets)	1/4	cup	shredded cheese
2 Tbs mayonnaise		1	tsp	Italian seasoning, (or dry basil)
2 Tbs plain Greek-style yogurt				

Procedure

1 Preheat oven to 375°.

2 Sprinkle both sides of catfish with salt and pepper. Place on a baking sheet which has been lined with foil and coated with cooking spray.

3 In a small bowl, mix remaining ingredients. Spread on top of catfish fillets to form a thick coating. Bake for 15 - 20 minutes or until top is brown.

Servings: 2

Preparation Time: 5 minutes
Cooking Time: 15 minutes

Nutrition Facts

Serving size: 1 catfish fillet

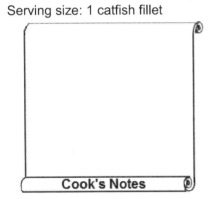

Cook's Notes

Amount Per Serving	
Calories	298.52
Calories From Fat (52%)	155.19
	% Daily Value
Total Fat 17.35g	27%
Saturated Fat 4.68g	23%
Cholesterol 99.34mg	33%
Sodium 440.19mg	18%
Potassium 524.37mg	15%
Total Carbohydrates 5.2g	2%
Fiber 0.1g	<1%
Sugar 1.03g	
Protein 28.92g	58%

Cioppino

An Italian-American fish stew from San Francisco from the late 1800s using a combination of crab meat, clams, shrimp, scallops, squid, mussels and fish. The cod, scallops and crab meat make an appearance in this version.

1/4	cup	olive oil
1/4	lb	pancetta, diced
1 large		shallot or 1 small yellow onion, finely diced
1		Fresno chili, minced (optional)
1	tsp	fresh garlic minced
1 small		bay leaf
2 small		celery stalks, finely diced
4 sprigs		fresh thyme
Salt and pepper to taste		

1/2	cup	sherry or dry white wine
1		(28 oz) can whole tomatoes, undrained
2 cups		chicken broth
6		basil leaves, torn
1	lb	cod fish pieces
1	lb	scallops
1	Tbs	Old Bay seasoning
1	lb	crab meat picked over for shells
1/4	cup	chopped fresh parsley for garnish

Procedure

1 In a Dutch oven heat olive oil on medium heat and render fat from pancetta, about 3 - 5 minutes.

2 Add shallots, chili pepper (if using), garlic, celery, bay leaf, thyme, salt and pepper and sauté until vegetables are tender, about 5 minutes.

3 Deglaze pan with sherry (or white wine) and reduce liquid by half. Add tomatoes (with their juice) mashing with a potato masher. Add stock and basil and simmer for about 10 minutes.

4 Season cod and scallops with Old Bay seasoning and gently drop them into pot. Simmer 8 - 10 minutes. Add the crab and gently heat through.

5 Serve in bowls garnished with chopped parsley and a piece of crusty bread for dunking.

Servings: 8

Preparation Time: 30 minutes
Cooking Time: 30 minutes

Nutrition Facts

Serving size: 1 ½ cups

Cook's Notes

Amount Per Serving	
Calories	297.33
Calories From Fat (44%)	129.83
	% Daily Value
Total Fat 14.53g	22%
Saturated Fat 3.36g	17%
Cholesterol 82.99mg	28%
Sodium 906.85mg	38%
Potassium 741.14mg	21%
Total Carbohydrates 7.54g	3%
Fiber 1.89g	8%
Sugar 1.32g	
Protein 29.45g	59%

Crab and Cheese Pie

Swap the crab with a 6 oz. can of salmon (or smoked salmon) for a different flavor. The texture of the batter using the biscuit mix makes the dish creamy and easy to swallow.

8 oz	crab meat, drained and picked over for shells	1 cup	biscuit mix
1 cup	grated sharp cheddar cheese	4 large	eggs
4 - 5	scallions, thinly sliced (white part and tips of green part)	1 Tbs	Dijon mustard
2 cups	milk	1 tsp	salt

Procedure

1. Preheat oven to 400°.
2. Coat a deep dish pie plate with cooking spray. Set on a baking sheet and set aside.
3. In a medium-size bowl, combine and mix crab, cheddar cheese and scallions together. Arrange mixture in pie plate.
4. In a blender purée milk, biscuit mix, eggs, mustard and salt until smooth, about 1 minute.
5. Pour batter carefully over crab mixture, bake for 40 - 45 minutes. Allow to rest 5 minutes before cutting and serving.

Servings: 8

Preparation Time: 15 minutes
Cooking Time: 45 minutes
Inactive Time: 5 minutes

Nutrition Facts

Serving size: 1/8 of pie

Cook's Notes

Amount Per Serving	
Calories	246.3
Calories From Fat (44%)	107.52
	% Daily Value
Total Fat 12g	18%
Saturated Fat 4.51g	23%
Cholesterol 137.02mg	46%
Sodium 881.12mg	37%
Potassium 319.6mg	9%
Total Carbohydrates 19.35g	6%
Fiber 1.72g	7%
Sugar 7.69g	
Protein 14.91g	30%

Crab Crème Brûlée

Crème Brûlée is typically served as a dessert but this decadent dish from Claire Robinson is great as a main course.

3	ears	fresh corn or 1 1/2 cups frozen corn, thawed	3	large	eggs
			2	large	egg yolks
2	cups	heavy (whipping) cream	1/2	lb	crab meat picked over for shells (or lobster meat)
1 1/2	tsp	salt			
1 1/2	tsp	pepper	2	oz	Parmigiano-Reggiano cheese, grated

Procedure

1 Preheat oven to 325°. Turn on kettle to boil water for water bath.

2 In a medium saucepan over medium heat combine corn kernels, cream, salt and pepper. Bring to a boil, then reduce heat and simmer for 3 to 5 minutes it thickens.

3 Whisk the eggs and yolks together in a mixing bowl. Stir in a little of the corn mixture to temper the eggs, then add remainder to corn mix.

4 Transfer the mixture to a blender and puree. Pass through a fine sieve into a bowl and discard any solids left in the strainer.

5 Place six 4 oz. ramekins in a 2" deep baking dish large enough to hold them and ladle in the corn mixture, dividing evenly.

6 Pour boiling water carefully into baking dish to reach half way up sides of ramekins.

7 Bake for approximately 35 minutes. There should be a slight jiggle when done. Remove from the oven and let cool for at least 10 minutes in the baking dish. Remove from water bath.

8 Top each ramekin with crab meat and sprinkle with the Parmigiano-Reggiano cheese. Place ramekins on a baking sheet and broil until cheese is brown and crisp.

Servings: 6
Preparation Time: 15 minutes
Cooking Time: 30 minutes

Nutrition Facts

Serving size: 1 ramekin

Cook's Notes

Amount Per Serving	
Calories	262.93
Calories From Fat (72%)	190.4
	% Daily Value
Total Fat 21.56g	33%
Saturated Fat 12.16g	61%
Cholesterol 225.46mg	75%
Sodium 885.47mg	37%
Potassium 178.86mg	5%
Total Carbohydrates 7.35g	2%
Fiber 0.79g	3%
Sugar 1.1g	
Protein 10.98g	22%

Crab Salad

Serve it in lettuce leaves or as an open-faced sandwich and grill a slice of cheese on top like a "tuna melt." My husband's choice of bread is the Green "Bread" (page 19) because it is so easy to swallow.

3.5	oz	crab meat, drained and picked over for shells
1	Tbs	mayonnaise
1	Tbs	sliced scallions

1	medium	radish, grated
2	tsp	Dijon mustard
		Salt and freshly ground black pepper to taste

Procedure

1 In a medium-size bowl flake crab. Add all other ingredients and mix thoroughly to combine.

2 Season with salt and pepper to taste and serve.

Servings: 1

Preparation Time: 10 minutes

Nutrition Facts

Cook's Notes

Amount Per Serving	
Calories	151.1
Calories From Fat (37%)	55.4
	% Daily Value
Total Fat 6.48g	10%
Saturated Fat 0.92g	5%
Cholesterol 100.07mg	33%
Sodium 633.51mg	26%
Potassium 288.41mg	8%
Total Carbohydrates 4.66g	2%
Fiber 0.24g	<1%
Sugar 1.08g	
Protein 18.75g	38%

Try it nestled into a bed of arame (seaweed) salad (page 111) - it's delicious!

2 large	portobello mushroom caps	4-5		scallions, sliced
1 cup	crab meat (about 4 oz.) picked over for shells	1/4	cup	chopped fresh cilantro or parsley
3 oz	cream cheese, softened (or Neufchatel or Boursin	1/4	cup	grated Parmesan cheese
		Salt and pepper to taste		
2 Tbs	plain Greek-style yogurt	2	slices	cheddar or muenster cheese

Procedure

1 Preheat oven to 375°.

2 Scrape out gills from mushrooms and set aside.

3 In a medium-size bowl combine crab meat, cream cheese, yogurt, scallions, cilantro and Parmesan. Season with salt and pepper.

4 Spoon stuffing into mushroom caps and cover with sliced cheese.

5 Place on a baking sheet lined with foil which has been coated with cooking spray and bake for 20 minutes or until cheese is lightly browned.

Servings: 2

Preparation Time: 15 minutes
Cooking Time: 20 minutes

Nutrition Facts

Serving size: 1mushroom cap

Amount Per Serving	
Calories	348.6
Calories From Fat (45%)	156.16
	% Daily Value
Total Fat 17.74g	27%
Saturated Fat 9.88g	49%
Cholesterol 111.73mg	37%
Sodium 492.05mg	21%
Potassium 671.58mg	19%
Total Carbohydrates 9.53g	3%
Fiber 1.28g	5%
Sugar 4.65g	
Protein 17.83g	36%

Cook's Notes

Any fish can be prepared in this manner and is a terrific low-fat option. Also, because the parchment captures the moisture, it is very easy on the throat. The length of cooking time should be adjusted according to the thickness of the fish.

4	medium	mushrooms, sliced thin
1	medium	zucchini, julienned
4		scallions (white part), julienned
1	medium	tomato, diced
1/4	cup	sliced roasted red peppers
1	Tbs	chopped fresh cilantro, dill, tarragon, or thyme

1 (8 oz)	catfish fillet cut in 2 pieces (or two 4 oz. white fish fillets)
2 tsp	olive oil
2 Tbs	clam juice (dry white wine, water or chicken broth)
	Salt and black pepper to taste

Procedure

1. Preheat oven to 375°.
2. Toss vegetables together and set aside..
3. Cut 2 pieces of parchment paper about 18" long. Fold each piece in half and cut into a heart shape.
4. Open paper hearts and arrange half of the vegetable mixture next to the fold of each heart. Sprinkle with salt and pepper and add 1/4 of the chopped herb. Arrange the fish fillet over the vegetables, and sprinkle with the olive oil and clam juice (or wine). Top with another 1/4 of the herb.
5. Fold the top half of one of the paper hearts over fish and vegetables and beginning with the rounded end, fold the edges of the paper over, twisting and folding to form an airtight packet.
6. Repeat with the second parchment heart. (The packets may be prepared up to 4 hours ahead and chilled.) Bring them back to room temperature before baking.
7. Slide packets onto a baking sheet and bake for about 12 minutes, or until the paper is puffed and browned lightly around the edges.
8. Carefully slide on to a warmed plate and serve immediately.

Preparation Time: 25 minutes   Cooking Time: 12 minutes
Servings: 2

Nutrition Facts

Serving size: 1packet

Cook's Notes

Amount Per Serving	
Calories	308.18
Calories From Fat (33%)	101.22
	% Daily Value
Total Fat 11.37g	17%
Saturated Fat 0.77g	4%
Cholesterol 98.58mg	33%
Sodium 436.85mg	18%
Potassium 1294.96mg	37%
Total Carbohydrates 15g	5%
Fiber 3.94g	16%
Sugar 7.82g	
Protein 37.42g	75%

Grilled Spiced White Fish

Use any white fish such as halibut, sole, tilapia or catfish.

2	(4 oz)	tilapia filets		1/2	tsp	chili powder
Salt and freshly ground black pepper to taste				2	tsp	crushed garlic
1/2	cup	plain Greek-style yogurt		1	Tbs	fresh lemon juice
2	tsp	garam masala		Lemon wedges to garnish		
1	tsp	ground coriander				

Procedure

1. Season fish on both sides with salt and pepper.
2. In a small bowl mix together remaining ingredients except lemon wedges. Pour over fish, turning to coat on both sides. Cover and refrigerate for several hours.
3. Remove fish from refrigerator, remove cover, and set aside to take the chill off.
4. Heat a grill pan on medium high heat, remove fish from marinade and allow excess to drip off fish. Place gently in grill pan and cook about 3 - 4 minutes per side (depending on type of fish and thickness).
5. Remove to serving plates and garnish with lemon wedges.

Servings: 2

Preparation Time: 5 minutes
Cooking Time: 8 minutes

Nutrition Facts

Serving size: 1 fish fillet

Cook's Notes

Amount Per Serving	
Calories	142.35
Calories From Fat (18%)	25.71
	% Daily Value
Total Fat 2.87g	4%
Saturated Fat 1.18g	6%
Cholesterol 53.46mg	18%
Sodium 140.11mg	6%
Potassium 478.33mg	14%
Total Carbohydrates 6.28g	2%
Fiber 0.69g	3%
Sugar 0.27g	
Protein 23.46g	47%

It doesn't get easier than this.

2 (4 oz)	salmon fillets with skin	1 Tbs maple syrup	
1 Tbs	grainy mustard	Salt and freshly ground black pepper to taste	

Procedure

1. Preheat oven broiler. Line a broiler pan with foil and coat with non-stick cooking spray. Set aside.
2. In a small bowl, combine mustard with maple syrup.
3. Sprinkle salmon filets with salt and pepper and place on broiler pan. Top with mustard mixture. Broil 4 - 5 minutes until it flakes easily and serve.

Servings: 2

Preparation Time: 5 minutes
Cooking Time: 5 minutes

Nutrition Facts

Serving size: 1 salmon fillet

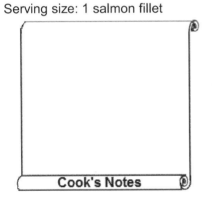

Cook's Notes

Amount Per Serving	
Calories	314.28
Calories From Fat (37%)	117.32
	% Daily Value
Total Fat 13.18g	20%
Saturated Fat 1.94g	10%
Cholesterol 108.9mg	36%
Sodium 335.74mg	14%
Potassium 1001.58mg	29%
Total Carbohydrates 7.24g	2%
Fiber 0.07g	<1%
Sugar 6.04g	
Protein 39.87g	80%

Scallops in Thousand Island

Serve this very simple dish with couscous or try my Kauli Pilaf made with cauliflower (page 156).

6 large   scallops, feet removed   1/4   cup   thousand island dressing

Procedure

1 Pull off the "feet" or little muscle from the scallops. Blot with paper towels to dry completely. Season both sides of scallops with salt and pepper.

2 Heat a medium-size non-stick skillet, coated with cooking spray sear the scallops on one side about 3 minutes until brown.

3 Turn them over and pour the dressing over and around scallops. Turn the heat down and simmer for another 2 - 3 minutes until scallops have cooked through and sauce is bubbly.

Servings: 2

Preparation Time: 5 minutes
Cooking Time: 10 minutes

Nutrition Facts

Serving size: 3 scallops

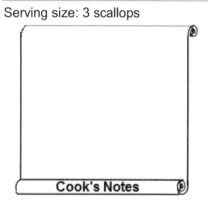

Cook's Notes

Amount Per Serving	
Calories	146.68
Calories From Fat (67%)	98.86
	% Daily Value
Total Fat 11.18g	17%
Saturated Fat 1.65g	8%
Cholesterol 18.93mg	6%
Sodium 446.09mg	19%
Potassium 125.69mg	4%
Total Carbohydrates 6.01g	2%
Fiber 0.25g	1%
Sugar 4.74g	
Protein 5.77g	12%

Recipe Tips

Also excellent with Green Goddess Dressing.

Author Notes

I like using Annie's Organic brand.

This is my adaptation of my god-daughter Annette Friesen's recipe.

2	Tbs	flour
1 1/2	Tbs	paprika (Hungarian sweet)
1	tsp	smoked paprika
1/2	tsp	chili powder
6 large		scallops, feet removed
1 large		red bell pepper, seeded and diced

2 Tbs		peanut oil (or canola oil) for frying
1 cup		salsa, chunky style
1 Tbs		red wine vinegar
1 medium		orange, freshly squeezed

Procedure

1. Pull off the "feet" or little muscle from the scallops. On a large plate mix together flour, paprika and chili powder. Dredge scallops, coating all over with flour mixture.
2. In a medium-size skillet heat oil on medium high heat. Sear scallops for 2 minutes on each side until brown. Transfer to serving plates.
3. Reduce heat to medium, add salsa, vinegar and orange juice, bring to a boil and stirring to combine flavors. Pour sauce over scallops and serve.

Servings: 2

Preparation Time: 5 minutes
Cooking Time: 5 minutes

Nutrition Facts

Serving size: 3 scallops

Cook's Notes

Amount Per Serving	
Calories	276.17
Calories From Fat (49%)	136.33
	% Daily Value
Total Fat 15.49g	24%
Saturated Fat 2.62g	13%
Cholesterol 10.8mg	4%
Sodium 974.5mg	41%
Potassium 911.11mg	26%
Total Carbohydrates 27.62g	9%
Fiber 7.25g	29%
Sugar 10.16g	
Protein 10.49g	21%

These are the easiest of all. Vegetables offer a wide variety of textures, colors and flavors. Thankfully my husband loves them all with the exception of the cabbage family. Of course when I make roast duck, the red cabbage makes an appearance and he takes his one obligatory spoonful.

Zucchini is an incredibly versatile vegetable that has very high internal moisture and makes an appearance regularly on our dinner plate in many different forms.

Kauli Pilaf (page 156) & White Sauce (page 132) with grilled salmon

Zucchini shredded and sautéed in butter

"French" Salad

The Hungarians call this "French" Salad, having nothing to do with French cooking. It's served typically at Easter time.

1 cup	frozen peas and carrots	3/4	cup	sour cream
1 small	parsnip, peeled and cut into 1/4" dice (about 1/3 cup)	2	tsp	Dijon mustard
2 large	hard-boiled eggs, chopped	1	tsp	fresh lemon juice
1 small	Granny Smith or Macintosh apple, cored, peeled and chopped	Salt and freshly ground black pepper to taste		

Procedure

1. Blanch vegetables in salted water until crisp tender, drain and allow to cool completely.
2. In a large mixing bowl, combine vegetable, eggs and apples.
3. In a medium-size bowl, combine sour cream, mustard, and lemon juice. Season to taste with salt and pepper, adding more lemon juice if desired.
4. Pour dressing over vegetable mixture and fold gently to combine. Chill until ready to serve.

Servings: 2

Preparation Time: 15 minutes
Cooking Time: 15 minutes
Inactive Time: 3 hours

Nutrition Facts

Serving size: about 1 cup

Cook's Notes

Amount Per Serving	
Calories	235.47
Calories From Fat (31%)	72.81
	% Daily Value
Total Fat 8.18g	13%
Saturated Fat 2.96g	15%
Cholesterol 192.03mg	64%
Sodium 212.14mg	9%
Potassium 498.39mg	14%
Total Carbohydrates 30.87g	10%
Fiber 7.27g	29%
Sugar 14.2g	
Protein 11.23g	22%

Author Notes

The parsnips and apple should add enough sweetness but if not, sprinkle in a touch of sugar or stevia. The dressing should be slightly tart however.

Blue Cheese Soufflé ½₂

The making of a soufflé is easy - really. All you have to remember is to be gentle when folding in the egg whites. It's that simple. I prefer serving them in individual ramekins.

3	Tbs	butter, divided	1/2	cup	blue cheese, mashed
2	Tbs	grated Parmesan cheese	Freshly grated nutmeg		
2	tsp	flour	2	large	eggs, separated
1/2	cup	milk	Pinch of salt		

Procedure

1 Heat oven to 375°. Butter two 8-ounce ramekins with 1 tablespoon of butter. Coat with Parmesan, tapping out excess. Set aside.

2 In a small saucepan over medium heat melt remaining butter. Stir in the flour and cook 1 minute. Whisk in the milk and cook, stirring constantly, until the sauce thickens, about 1 minute.

3 Remove from heat and stir in mashed cheese until melted. Grate in nutmeg, whisk in yolks one at a time and set aside.

4 In a small bowl, beat egg whites with salt until stiff peaks form. Stir 1/4 of the egg whites into cheese sauce to lighten it. Gently fold in remaining egg whites. Spoon into prepared ramekins and arrange on a small baking sheet. Bake until puffed and brown, about 20 minutes. Serve immediately.

Servings: 2

Preparation Time: 15 minutes
Cooking Time: 20 minutes

Nutrition Facts

Serving size: 1 soufflé

Cook's Notes

Amount Per Serving	
Calories	386.92
Calories From Fat (75%)	288.74
	% Daily Value
Total Fat 32.7g	50%
Saturated Fat 19.53g	98%
Cholesterol 260.78mg	87%
Sodium 711.21mg	30%
Potassium 244.94mg	7%
Total Carbohydrates 6.71g	2%
Fiber 0.1g	<1%
Sugar 3.66g	
Protein 16.75g	34%

Recipe Tips

You can use Gruyere or Cheddar if you prefer but NO peeking while baking.

With its light licorice flavor it is a perfect blend with tomatoes. This is one of our favorites.

1 large	fennel bulb, stalks removed, cut in quarters	1 (14 oz)	can diced tomatoes, undrained
1 Tbs	olive oil	8 large	green olives (pimento-stuffed), sliced
1 large	red onion, thinly sliced	3 Tbs	capers
		2 Tbs	chopped parsley

Procedure

1. Cut the fennel in quarters, cut out core and discard.
2. In a large skillet, heat the olive oil over moderate heat, add the fennel and cook turning to lightly brown all sides.
3. Add the onions and cook stirring and shaking the pan so as not to break up the fennel.
4. Add the tomatoes with their liquid, olives and capers. Cover and simmer on low until fork tender. Add water to prevent sticking.
5. Stir in chopped parsley and serve.

Servings: 4

Preparation Time: 10 minutes
Cooking Time: 20 minutes

Nutrition Facts

Serving size: 1/4 fennel bulb with sauce

Cook's Notes

Amount Per Serving	
Calories	270.06
Calories From Fat (78%)	210.12
	% Daily Value
Total Fat 24.52g	38%
Saturated Fat 3.23g	16%
Cholesterol 0mg	0%
Sodium 2829.27mg	118%
Potassium 119.36mg	3%
Total Carbohydrates 14.36g	5%
Fiber 7.34g	29%
Sugar 0.04g	
Protein 1.85g	4%

Leftovers will last for days when refrigerated and it reheats well.

2 Tbs	olive oil	2		bay leaves
1 medium	sweet onion. thinly sliced	1/2	cup	chicken stock
2	Granny Smith apples, halved, cored and thinly sliced	1/3	cup	apple cider vinegar
		1	Tbs	maple syrup (or agave syrup)
1 head	red cabbage, cored and shredded			Salt and freshly ground black pepper to taste
1 Tbs	chopped fresh dill			

Procedure

1 In a large nonstick skillet heat olive oil on medium heat. Sauté onions and apples until they begin to soften, 2 - 3 minutes.

2 Add the cabbage, dill, bay leaves, and broth. Cover and simmer, stirring occasionally until cabbage softens, 20 - 25 minutes.

3 Stir maple syrup into vinegar, pour over cabbage and stir, adding salt & pepper to taste. Serve garnished with a few dill sprigs.

Servings: 12

Preparation Time: 15 minutes
Cooking Time: 30 minutes

Nutrition Facts

Serving size: About ½ cup

Cook's Notes

Amount Per Serving	
Calories	61.09
Calories From Fat (36%)	22.02
	% Daily Value
Total Fat 2.49g	4%
Saturated Fat 0.35g	2%
Cholesterol 0mg	0%
Sodium 45.43mg	2%
Potassium 241.59mg	7%
Total Carbohydrates 9.33g	3%
Fiber 2.45g	10%
Sugar 3.84g	
Protein 1.28g	3%

Celeriac Mash

This is a very versatile vegetable. Think of celeriac as potatoes. You can combine it with parsnips, cauliflower or other root vegetables. I've even added a peeled Granny Smith apple for a bit of a new twist (see recipe tips).

1		celeriac, peeled and cut into 1/2" cubes	1/2	cup	plain Greek-style yogurt, cream cheese or heavy cream
4	cups	water	2	Tbs	chopped fresh parsley
1/2	tsp	salt			

Procedure

1. Place diced celeriac in a medium-size saucepan and add cold water (celeriac will float in the water). Bring to a boil, add salt and simmer partly covered until tender (15 - 20 minutes).
2. Drain and return to saucepan on a very low flame and cook while gently shaking the pan for a few minutes to evaporate any excess liquid.
3. Pour into the bowl of a food processor fitted with a metal blade and process until nearly smooth. Add yogurt, cream cheese or heavy cream and process until completely smooth.
4. Add chopped parsley and pulse several times to incorporate.

Servings: 4

Preparation Time: 5 minutes
Cooking Time: 25 minutes

Nutrition Facts

Serving size: a heaping ½ cup

Cook's Notes

Amount Per Serving	
Calories	183.45
Calories From Fat (21%)	37.93
	% Daily Value
Total Fat 4.32g	7%
Saturated Fat 2.74g	14%
Cholesterol 16.43mg	5%
Sodium 598.26mg	25%
Potassium 717.26mg	20%
Total Carbohydrates 21.65g	7%
Fiber 0.06g	<1%
Sugar 17.26g	
Protein 14.78g	30%

Recipe Tips

To peel this poor ugly vegetable, cut off both ends, lay it flat on a cutting board and cut the knobby peel away from top to bottom. If adding an apple, add it half way through the boiling process otherwise they'll turn to mush.

Celeriac-Parsnip Cloud

If the celeriac has fresh green leaves on it I use them instead of parsley to enhance the flavor of this underrated vegetable. When it is served, it looks like a lovely white cloud with green flecks in it.

1 medium	celeriac, peeled and cut into 1/2" cubes	2	Tbs	heavy (whipping) cream
1 medium	parsnip, peeled and cut into 1/2" dice	2	Tbs	plain Greek-style yogurt
1 small	garlic clove, crushed	1/4	cup	chopped fresh parsley

Procedure

1. In a medium-size saucepan combine celeriac, parsnip and garlic. Add enough water to cover, place a lid on and bring to a boil.
2. Add salt and simmer until tender, 15 - 20 minutes. Drain and return to saucepan on a very low flame and cook while gently shaking the pan for a few minutes to evaporate any excess liquid.
3. Pour into the bowl of a food processor fitted with a metal blade and process until nearly smooth. Add cream and yogurt and process until completely smooth adding more heavy cream or yogurt to achieve desired consistency.
4. Add chopped parsley and pulse several times to incorporate.

Servings: 4

Preparation Time: 15 minutes
Cooking Time: 30 minutes

Nutrition Facts

Serving size: ½ cup

Cook's Notes

Amount Per Serving	
Calories	74.27
Calories From Fat (37%)	27.33
	% Daily Value
Total Fat 3.12g	5%
Saturated Fat 1.84g	9%
Cholesterol 10.65mg	4%
Sodium 52.74mg	2%
Potassium 288.96mg	8%
Total Carbohydrates 10.8g	4%
Fiber 2.47g	10%
Sugar 2.81g	
Protein 1.7g	3%

Fennel with Tomatoes

This is one of my super easy side dishes.

1	(14.5 oz.)	can diced tomatoes, liquid reserved	1	medium	fennel bulb, stalks removed, cut in quarters, sliced crosswise
1/2	cup	free range, low sodium, chicken broth			Salt and freshly ground pepper to taste

Procedure

1. In a medium-size sauce pan, bring reserved tomato juice and chicken broth to a simmer. Add fennel slices, cover and simmer for 15 - 20 minutes until nearly soft.
2. Add tomatoes, more stock or water if necessary, season with salt and freshly ground pepper and continue to simmer until vegetables are completely tender.

Servings: 4

Preparation Time: 10 minutes
Cooking Time: 30 minutes

Nutrition Facts

Serving size: about ½ cup

Cook's Notes

Amount Per Serving	
Calories	56.64
Calories From Fat (8%)	4.28
	% Daily Value
Total Fat 0.49g	<1%
Saturated Fat 0.05g	<1%
Cholesterol 0mg	0%
Sodium 193.3mg	8%
Potassium 571.82mg	16%
Total Carbohydrates 12.72g	4%
Fiber 3.95g	16%
Protein 2.7g	5%

Recipe Tips

Add a teaspoon of your favorite dry herb such as basil, thyme or Italian seasoning before simmering.

Use frozen spinach or other greens of choice in place of collards. Also, any leftovers are great used in a frittata or as a filling in omelets.

2	Tbs	lightly salted butter	1 (6 oz)		jar artichoke hearts, drained and quartered
2	Tbs	red onion, diced			
1/2	tsp	minced garlic	16 oz		frozen collard greens, thawed, drained, and chopped
4	oz	prosciutto, thinly sliced, diced into 1/2-inch pieces (about 1/2 cup)			Salt and freshly ground black pepper to taste

Procedure

1 In a large nonstick skillet melt butter on medium heat. Sauté onions until soft, about 5 minutes. Stir in garlic and prosciutto and cook another minute or two.

2 Add remaining ingredients and continue to cook until everything is heated through. Season with salt and freshly ground pepper and serve.

Servings: 6

Preparation Time: 10 minutes
Cooking Time: 10 minutes

Nutrition Facts

Serving size: About ½ cup

Cook's Notes

Amount Per Serving	
Calories	110.24
Calories From Fat (46%)	50.98
	% Daily Value
Total Fat 5.72g	9%
Saturated Fat 3g	15%
Cholesterol 23.41mg	8%
Sodium 598.91mg	25%
Potassium 363.2mg	10%
Total Carbohydrates 8.39g	3%
Fiber 3.46g	14%
Sugar 0.33g	
Protein 8.12g	16%

Herbed Flan with Caviar

This was inspired by an Emeril Lagasse recipe. It's simple, soft and delicate.

1/4	cup	milk
1/4	cup	heavy (whipping) cream
2	Tbs	snipped chives
1/4	tsp	salt

Pinch of white pepper		
2	large	egg yolks
1/2	oz	salmon roe (caviar)
2	tsp	crème fraîche (or sour cream)
1/2	tsp	lemon zest

Procedure

1 Preheat oven to 275°. Put a kettle on to boil water.

2 In a small saucepan combine milk, cream and lemon zest. Heat until small bubbles form on side of the pan. Set aside for 5 to 10 minutes.

3 Place the chives and warm milk in a blender and puree until smooth. Strain through a fine mesh sieve, discard solids. Add salt and white pepper to taste.

4 In a small bowl, lightly whisk egg yolks. Add the milk in a steady stream, whisking gently to create a smooth custard.

5 Transfer custard into a 4 oz. ramekin and place into a loaf pan.

6 Set loaf pan on top of a small baking sheet. Fill loaf pan 1/2 way up the ramekin with boiling hot water from kettle. Cover with foil, carefully lift into oven and bake for 45 minutes to 1 hour or until custard is set but still slightly jiggly in center.

7 Remove from oven and allow to cool in water bath for 10 minutes. Serve half per person, garnishing with a dollop of salmon roe (caviar), crème fraîche and chives.

Servings: 2

Preparation Time: 10 minutes
Cooking Time: 1 hour

Nutrition Facts

Serving size: 2 oz.

Cook's Notes

Amount Per Serving	
Calories	199.42
Calories From Fat (80%)	159.88
	% Daily Value
Total Fat 18.03g	28%
Saturated Fat 9.85g	49%
Cholesterol 258.61mg	86%
Sodium 333.27mg	14%
Potassium 113.97mg	3%
Total Carbohydrates 3.79g	1%
Fiber 0.26g	1%
Sugar 1.73g	
Protein 6.19g	12%

Kauli Pilaf

There is a favorite rice dish in Hungary called Rizy-Bizy. Rice is combined with peas and carrots. Here the cauliflower plays the role of the rice and makes a spectacular transformation. Sometimes I add frozen carrots and peas to remind me of Rizy Bizy. This idea comes from George Stella.

2 cups	grated raw cauliflower	2		bay leaves
1 Tbs	unsalted butter	1	cup	chicken broth
1 Tbs	olive oil	1/2	tsp	turmeric
1 small	shallot or 1 small yellow onion, finely diced	1/2	tsp	salt
		1/4	tsp	freshly ground black pepper
1 tsp	minced garlic	1	cup	frozen peas and carrots

Procedure

1. Using the large grating blade of a food processor, grate cauliflower (or use a box grater).
2. In a large nonstick skillet heat the butter and oil over medium-high heat. Add onions, cauliflower, garlic, and bay leaves and cook for about 5 minutes while stirring.
3. Add 3/4 cup of the chicken broth and seasonings and simmer until crisp tender, 5 - 10 minutes. Add frozen peas and carrots during the last 5 minutes of cooking and add remainder of chicken stock or water if mixture is too dry. Do not allow cauliflower to get too soggy.

Servings: 4

Preparation Time: 15 minutes
Cooking Time: 10 minutes

Nutrition Facts

Serving size: about ½ cup

Cook's Notes

Amount Per Serving	
Calories	85.23
Calories From Fat (69%)	58.41
	% Daily Value
Total Fat 6.61g	10%
Saturated Fat 2.35g	12%
Cholesterol 7.63mg	3%
Sodium 923.47mg	38%
Potassium 204.89mg	6%
Total Carbohydrates 5.79g	2%
Fiber 1.72g	7%
Sugar 0.97g	
Protein 1.92g	4%

We love Indian food. Bal Arneson made this on the Food Channel and I love the combination of spices because they are pungent but not spicy. Risotto is usually served "al dente" but I cook mine until it is softer and easier to swallow.

4 cups	chicken stock		5 whole	star anise
6 Tbs	unsalted butter		2 cups	thinly sliced mushrooms,
1 small	sweet onion, finely chopped			(shiitake, oyster, portobello)
1 Tbs	garam masala		1 cup	arborio rice
1 tsp	cardamom pods		1/2 cup	white wine
1 tsp	mustard seeds		Salt and pepper to taste	
			Parmesan cheese, shaved	

Procedure

1. In a medium-size saucepan bring chicken stock to a boil, turn down to low, and keep warm.

2. In another medium-size saucepan, melt 4 tablespoons of butter over medium heat, stir in the onions and sauté until translucent, 3 - 4 minutes.

3. Add garam masala, cardamom pods, mustard seeds, and star anise. Stir to combine and cook for about 1 minute until spices release their flavor.

4. Stir in mushrooms and cook until they begin to caramelize and get brown, about 5 minutes. Add arborio rice stirring until rice is coated with butter. Pour in wine and continue stirring until absorbed by rice.

5. Begin adding hot stock 1 ladle at a time, stirring until absorbed before adding next ladle. Continue stirring and adding stock until rice is completely soft and creamy, 25 - 30 minutes. Turn off heat, season with salt and freshly ground pepper and whisk in remaining 2 tablespoons of butter until melted and shiny. Serve with the shaved Parmesan.

Servings: 4

Preparation Time: 15 minutes
Cooking Time: 45 minutes

Nutrition Facts

Serving size: a generous ½ cup

Cook's Notes

Amount Per Serving	
Calories	811.49
Calories From Fat (38%)	309.18
	% Daily Value
Total Fat 38g	58%
Saturated Fat 12.67g	63%
Cholesterol 45.8mg	15%
Sodium 149.73mg	6%
Potassium 1996.01mg	57%
Total Carbohydrates 106.79g	36%
Fiber 19.2g	77%
Sugar 2.19g	
Protein 28.07g	56%

Recipe Tips

Fish out the cardamom pods and star anise before serving.

Potato Vegetable Pancakes

German potato pancakes are a real treat. Here is a heartier version with a bright assortment of vegetables.

1 medium	baking potato, peeled	2	large	eggs, lightly beaten
1 medium	carrot, peeled	1	tsp	salt
1 medium	zucchini	1/4	tsp	freshly ground black pepper
1 small	red onion, quartered	2	Tbs	vegetable or canola oil
2 Tbs	quinoa flour			

Procedure

1. In a food processor fitted with the large shredding disk, shred vegetables. Transfer to a large bowl, stir in quinoa flour, eggs, salt and pepper. Mix well.
2. In a large nonstick skillet, heat oil over medium high heat. Using a large spoon or ice cream scoop, arrange 6 portions into the skillet and flatten them into round pancakes. Cook over medium heat until brown on one side, about 10 minutes. Turn them over and cook an additional 8 - 9 minutes. Serve immediately or keep warm in the oven until serving time.

Servings: 6

Preparation Time: 10 minutes
Cooking Time: 20 minutes

Nutrition Facts

Serving size: 1 pancake

Cook's Notes

Amount Per Serving	
Calories	66.82
Calories From Fat (25%)	16.75
	% Daily Value
Total Fat 1.86g	3%
Saturated Fat 0.56g	3%
Cholesterol 62mg	21%
Sodium 348.91mg	15%
Potassium 282.46mg	8%
Total Carbohydrates 9.26g	3%
Fiber 1.29g	5%
Sugar 1.36g	
Protein 3.53g	7%

Ratatouille ⅔

This fast and easy side dish was given to me by my friend Elaine Sterling. I use Japanese eggplant because it has a milder flavor.

1 tsp	olive oil	1	small	red onion, thinly sliced
1 small	Japanese eggplant, peeled and diced	1	pint	grape tomatoes (or cherry)
1 medium	zucchini or yellow squash, halved lengthwise and cut crosswise into 1/2-inch pieces	1/2	cup	French salad dressing of choice
		1	Tbs	capers, drained (optional)
1 medium	bell pepper, chopped (red, yellow or orange)	Salt and pepper to taste		

Procedure

1 In a medium skillet heat olive oil, sauté all vegetables on medium low heat, except tomatoes, until tender, about 10 minutes. Add a little water if skillet becomes too dry and cover.

2 Add tomatoes, cover and cook until tomatoes are warmed through. Add capers, if using, and season with salt and pepper to taste.

Servings: 4

Preparation Time: 10 minutes
Cooking Time: 10 minutes

Nutrition Facts

Serving size: about 1 cup

Cook's Notes

Amount Per Serving	
Calories	184.86
Calories From Fat (69%)	127.69
	% Daily Value
Total Fat 14.48g	22%
Saturated Fat 1.79g	9%
Cholesterol 0mg	0%
Sodium 334.97mg	14%
Potassium 372.55mg	11%
Total Carbohydrates 13.73g	5%
Fiber 2.8g	11%
Sugar 7.42g	
Protein 1.88g	4%

Recipe Tips

Also works well with Thousand Island, Green Goddess or Low-fat French dressing.

These are a sweet version of German Potato Pancakes that makes a lovely side dish.

1	small	sweet potato, peeled	2	large	eggs , lightly beaten
1	medium	parsnip, peeled	1	tsp	salt
1	small	onion, quartered	1/4	tsp	freshly ground black pepper
2	Tbs	almond meal	2	Tbs	coconut oil (or vegetable oil)

Procedure

1 In a food processor fitted with the large shredding disk, shred vegetables. Transfer to a large bowl, stir in almond flour, eggs, salt and pepper. Mix well.

2 In a large nonstick skillet, heat oil over medium high heat. Using a large spoon or ice cream scoop, arrange 4 portions into the skillet and flatten them into round pancakes. Cook over medium heat until brown on one side, 8 - 10 minutes. Turn them over and cook an additional 8 - 9 minutes. Serve immediately or keep warm in the oven until serving time.

Servings: 4

Preparation Time: 10 minutes
Cooking Time: 20 minutes

Nutrition Facts

Serving size: 1 pancake

Cook's Notes

Amount Per Serving	
Calories	169.74
Calories From Fat (48%)	82.21
	% Daily Value
Total Fat 9.44g	15%
Saturated Fat 6.7g	34%
Cholesterol 93mg	31%
Sodium 512.62mg	21%
Potassium 466.93mg	13%
Total Carbohydrates 17.88g	6%
Fiber 3.45g	14%
Sugar 1.88g	
Protein 4.31g	9%

The dried cranberries add just the right amount of sweetness to this side dish.

1 bunch	Swiss chard, kale or mustard greens	3 Tbs dried cranberries, currants or raisins
1 Tbs	olive oil	1 Tbs balsamic vinegar
2	garlic cloves, minced	Salt and freshly ground pepper to taste

Procedure

1 Remove stalks from Swiss chard.

2 In a large pot of boiling salted water, cook chard (or other greens) until tender, 5 - 8 minutes. Drain and blot dry with paper towels.

3 In a large skillet heat olive oil on medium high heat, add garlic and stir for 30 seconds. Add chard, dried cranberries and stir to heat through, 3 - 5 minutes. Drizzle in vinegar and toss to coat, season with salt and freshly ground pepper.

Servings: 2

Preparation Time: 10 minutes
Cooking Time: 10 minutes

Nutrition Facts

Serving size: about ½ cup

Cook's Notes

Amount Per Serving	
Calories	264.83
Calories From Fat (26%)	67.96
	% Daily Value
Total Fat 7.68g	12%
Saturated Fat 0.94g	5%
Cholesterol 0mg	0%
Sodium 42.87mg	2%
Potassium 115.07mg	3%
Total Carbohydrates 48.62g	16%
Fiber 3.97g	16%
Sugar 1.42g	
Protein 0.55g	1%

Red Potatoes with Basil Vinaigrette

This was inspired by a recipe given to me by a co-worker Lucia Pintauro, back in our Clairol days of the 90's. Her original recipe made the pesto from scratch but I find this easier and faster. Sorry Lu...

1 1/4	lb	red potatoes, diced	1 Tbs Dijon mustard
1/4	cup	prepared pesto sauce	Salt and freshly ground black pepper to taste
1 1/2	Tbs	sherry vinegar	

Procedure

1 In a medium size saucepan boil potatoes in salted water until fork tender, 15 - 20 minutes. Drain and set aside.

2 In a medium-size bowl combine pesto, vinegar, mustard, salt and pepper, add potatoes, tossing gently so potatoes don't break apart.

3 Serve warm or at room temperature.

Servings: 6

Preparation Time: 10 minutes
Cooking Time: 20 minutes

Nutrition Facts

Serving size: about 4 oz.

Cook's Notes

Amount Per Serving	
Calories	78.4
Calories From Fat (2%)	1.78
	% Daily Value
Total Fat 0.21g	<1%
Saturated Fat 0.02g	<1%
Cholesterol 0mg	0%
Sodium 37.38mg	2%
Potassium 537.91mg	15%
Total Carbohydrates 17.66g	6%
Fiber 1.67g	7%
Sugar 0.2g	
Protein 2.14g	4%

White Bean Purée

I sneak beans into my husband's diet sometimes. He thinks he doesn't like them but when they're disguised, taste good and are easy to swallow, he loves them.

1	Tbs	unsalted butter
2	Tbs	finely diced onion
1	tsp	minced garlic
1	sprig	thyme

1 (15-oz)		can white beans, drained and rinsed
1/2	cup	free range, low-sodium chicken broth

Salt and pepper to taste

Procedure

1. In a medium saucepan on moderate heat, melt butter. Sauté onion, garlic and thyme sprig until onion is soft, about 5 minutes.
2. Add beans and broth and simmer until broth is reduced by half, about 5 minutes. Discard thyme sprig.
3. Purée in a small food processor, season with salt and pepper and serve hot.

Servings: 2

Preparation Time: 10 minutes
Cooking Time: 15 minutes

Nutrition Facts

Serving size: about ½ cup

Cook's Notes

Amount Per Serving	
Calories	174.79
Calories From Fat (32%)	55.9
	% Daily Value
Total Fat 6.35g	10%
Saturated Fat 3.72g	19%
Cholesterol 15.27mg	5%
Sodium 31.09mg	1%
Potassium 382.78mg	11%
Total Carbohydrates 22.18g	7%
Fiber 5.92g	24%
Sugar 0.73g	
Protein 8.2g	16%

Zucchini with Tomatoes #2

This is another one of my quick "go to" side dishes.

2 small	zucchini or yellow squash, halved lengthwise and cut crosswise into 1/2" pieces	1 (14.5 oz)	can stewed tomatoes, liquid reserved
		1 tsp	dried basil
		Salt and pepper to taste	

Procedure

1. In a medium-size sauce pan bring reserved tomato juice to a simmer, add zucchini, cover and simmer 5 - 8 minutes or until squash starts to soften.
2. Add stewed tomatoes, dried basil and continue to simmer until vegetables are soft and liquid is nearly evaporated. Season with salt and pepper and serve.

Servings: 4

Preparation Time: 10 minutes
Cooking Time: 15 minutes

Nutrition Facts

Serving size: about ½ cup

Cook's Notes

Amount Per Serving	
Calories	31.4
Calories From Fat (6%)	2.03
	% Daily Value
Total Fat 0.24g	<1%
Saturated Fat 0.04g	<1%
Cholesterol 0mg	0%
Sodium 255.71mg	11%
Potassium 254.51mg	7%
Total Carbohydrates 7.42g	2%
Fiber 1.32g	5%
Sugar 4.14g	
Protein 1.16g	2%

S oups happen to be a favorite food for us and here are some of our most cherished recipes. This section introduces the Hungarian "Főzelék" category (pronounced foz-eh-lake). It is not quite a soup but it's not really a stew either. It is cooked simply, typically by simmering, and is often thickened with a roux or slurry. It is frequently eaten as the main course for lunch or as garnish for roasted meats. It is an ideal meal for introducing more solid food as swallowing ability improves.

Carrot-Coriander Creamy Soup (page 174)

Chilled Avocado Cream Soup (page 176)

165

Allium Bisque

The generic name Allium is the Latin word for garlic. By adding potatoes this makes a hearty, delicious soup.

1	Tbs	unsalted butter	1	tsp	salt
1	Tbs	olive oil	1		bay leaf
2	large	red onions, diced	1/2	tsp	dried basil
2	medium	leeks, thinly sliced (white part only)	1/2	tsp	dried oregano
			1/4	tsp	dried marjoram
2	medium	shallots, finely chopped	5	cups	free range chicken broth
4	large	garlic cloves, minced	1		scallion, thinly sliced (white part and tips of green part)
2	medium	Yukon Gold potatoes, peeled and cubed			

Procedure

1 In a large soup pot over medium heat, melt together butter and oil. Add onions, leek, shallots and garlic. Sauté until lightly brown, about 10 minutes.

2 Add potatoes, salt, bay leaf and dried herbs. Stir to combine. Add chicken stock, bring to a boil, reduce heat, cover and simmer until potatoes are tender, about 30 minutes.

3 Ladle into bowls and sprinkle with scallions.

Servings: 4

Preparation Time: 15 minutes
Cooking Time: 30 minutes

Nutrition Facts

Serving size: about 1 ¼ cups

Cook's Notes

Amount Per Serving	
Calories	217.67
Calories From Fat (30%)	64.76
	% Daily Value
Total Fat 7.21g	11%
Saturated Fat 2.35g	12%
Cholesterol 7.63mg	3%
Sodium 743.17mg	31%
Potassium 583.66mg	17%
Total Carbohydrates 34.44g	11%
Fiber 3.83g	15%
Sugar 3.08g	
Protein 4.99g	10%

A delicious creamy soup that is sure to please.

1 Tbs unsalted butter	4 cups chicken broth
1 Tbs olive oil	5 oz Boursin cheese, at room
1 medium leek, white and light green part	temperature
halved lengthwise & thinly sliced	1 Tbs chopped fresh tarragon
2 tsp crushed garlic	Salt and pepper to taste
1 tsp dried marjoram	Flax oil for drizzling (optional)
2 cups asparagus pieces, (2-inch	
lengths) (about 1 lb)	
1/2 cup quinoa flakes	

Procedure

1 In a large soup pot melt together butter and olive oil over medium heat. Add leeks and cook for several minutes until softened. Add garlic and cook for about 30 seconds, stirring to combine.

2 Sprinkle in the marjoram, asparagus quinoa flakes and broth, stir to combine.

3 Cover and bring to a boil, reduce heat to very low and simmer for 15 - 20 minutes until asparagus is tender. Quarter the Boursin and add to pot stirring until thoroughly melted, about 5 minutes.

4 Add fresh tarragon, season with salt and pepper to taste. Allow to cool for a few minutes.

5 Serve as is or purée soup using a handheld immersion blender, or use a regular blender for a completely smooth soup.

Servings: 6

Preparation Time: 6 minutes
Cooking Time: 20 minutes

Nutrition Facts

Serving size: about 1 cup

Cook's Notes

Amount Per Serving	
Calories	209.2
Calories From Fat (64%)	134.68
	% Daily Value
Total Fat 15.66g	24%
Saturated Fat 8.72g	44%
Cholesterol 32.65mg	11%
Sodium 238.52mg	10%
Potassium 129.81mg	4%
Total Carbohydrates 13.89g	5%
Fiber 1.45g	6%
Sugar 0.74g	
Protein 4.74g	9%

The grain farro can be used in lieu of barley. Both grains are about the same size and have the same cooking time. Either way, it's a hearty delicious soup.

2 Tbs	olive oil		10	fresh thyme sprigs
1 large	onion, thinly sliced		2	bay leaves
2	leeks, white and light green part thinly sliced		1 1/2 lb	celeriac, peeled and cut into 1/2" cubes
2	garlic cloves, minced		1 lb	parsnips, peeled and cut into 1/2" dice
1 cup	uncooked barley			
8 cups	free range, low sodium, chicken broth		Salt and pepper to taste	
			1 lb	baby spinach
4 cups	water		1 tsp	grated nutmeg

Procedure

1 Heat olive oil in a large pot. Add the onion, leeks and garlic and cook over moderate heat, stirring occasionally, until tender, about 5 minutes.

2 Stir in barley, broth, water, thyme and bay leaves and bring to a boil.

3 Add the celeriac and parsnips and season with salt and pepper. Cover and simmer over low heat until the barley and vegetables are tender, about 40 minutes.

4 Stir in spinach, grate in nutmeg and stir to combine and wilt spinach. Allow soup to sit for a few minutes before serving.

Servings: 8

Preparation Time: 20 minutes
Cooking Time: 1 hour

Nutrition Facts

Serving size: about 1 ¼ cups

Cook's Notes

Amount Per Serving	
Calories	266.43
Calories From Fat (19%)	49.98
	% Daily Value
Total Fat 5.86g	9%
Saturated Fat 1.16g	6%
Cholesterol 0mg	0%
Sodium 202.02mg	8%
Potassium 1015.35mg	29%
Total Carbohydrates 46.94g	16%
Fiber 9.8g	39%
Sugar 6.49g	
Protein 10.86g	22%

Black Bean Soup

I love black bean soup. The combination of coriander and cumin is one of my favorites.

1	Tbs	olive oil	1/2	tsp	salt
1/2	medium	onion, finely chopped	1	tsp	ground coriander
1/4	cup	thinly sliced baby carrots	1/2	tsp	ground cumin
1/4	cup	1/4" diced peeled parsnips	1(15 oz)		can black beans, drained and rinsed
1/4	cup	1/4" diced celery	2	cups	chicken broth
1		bay leaf	1	Tbs	chopped fresh cilantro

Procedure

1. In a medium-size saucepan heat olive oil on medium heat. Sauté onions, carrots, parsnips, and celery for about 5 minutes, until vegetables are tender.
2. Add bay leaf, salt, coriander, cumin and salt. Stir and continue to sauté for another few minutes to release the flavor of the spices. Stir in drained black beans.
3. Turn up the heat and pour in the chicken broth. Cover and bring to a boil, reduce heat to low and simmer for 15 - 20 minutes until the beans and vegetables are very tender.
4. Allow to cool for about 10 minutes. Then discard bay leaf and ladle half the mixture into a blender and purée until smooth. Add the mixture back into the saucepan and stir to combine. Taste and adjust seasonings.
5. Ladle into serving bowls and top with cilantro and a dollop of sour cream if desired.

Servings: 2

Preparation Time: 15 minutes
Cooking Time: 30 minutes

Nutrition Facts

Serving size: about 1 ½ cups

Cook's Notes

Amount Per Serving	
Calories	416.73
Calories From Fat (34%)	143.49
	% Daily Value
Total Fat 16.2g	25%
Saturated Fat 2.53g	13%
Cholesterol 0mg	0%
Sodium 1742.41mg	73%
Potassium 996.55mg	28%
Total Carbohydrates 48.73g	16%
Fiber 17.06g	68%
Sugar 3.04g	
Protein 20.96g	42%

Author Notes

Purée the entire batch and even strain it if a really smooth consistency is necessary for easy swallowing.

Blue Cheese Soup

Emeril Lagasse adds Tawny Port and crumbled bacon bits before serving but the soup is delicious without it. It has become one of our favorites.

1 1/2	Tbs	unsalted butter	1	small	bay leaf
1 large		onion, thinly sliced	2	cups	free range, low sodium chicken broth
1/2	tsp	minced garlic			
1 1/2	lb	Yukon Gold potatoes, peeled and cubed	1/2	cup	light cream
			1/4	cup	heavy (whipping) cream
1/2	tsp	salt	1/2	cup	crumbled blue cheese
1/4	tsp	white pepper to taste	1	tsp	chopped fresh thyme leaves

Procedure

1. In a medium-size skillet over medium high heat, melt butter and sauté onions until just beginning to caramelize, about 10 minutes.
2. Add garlic and stir for 30 seconds. Add potatoes, salt, pepper and bay leaf. Continue to sauté for an additional 3 - 5 minutes.
3. Add broth, bring to a boil, cover, reduce heat to low and simmer until potatoes are tender, about 30 minutes.
4. Discard bay leaf. Remove from heat, purée with hand-held immersion blender or in batches in a food processor until smooth.
5. Stir in creams, reheat gently and whisk in blue cheese and thyme just until cheese melts. Adjust seasonings.
6. Ladle into soup bowls and top with additional small amount of blue cheese if desired.

Servings: 4

Preparation Time: 15 minutes
Cooking Time: 45 minutes

Nutrition Facts

Serving size: about 1 cup

Cook's Notes

Amount Per Serving	
Calories	396.43
Calories From Fat (44%)	176.32
	% Daily Value
Total Fat 20.01g	31%
Saturated Fat 12.44g	62%
Cholesterol 62.26mg	21%
Sodium 577.06mg	24%
Potassium 1321.65mg	38%
Total Carbohydrates 47.23g	16%
Fiber 3.6g	14%
Sugar 1.73g	
Protein 9.36g	19%

Butternut Squash Soup

The grated ginger was too spicy for my husband but the soup is wonderful without it.

1	(12oz)	butternut squash, peeled, seeded, and cut into 1-inch cubes	2	cups	chicken broth
1	Tbs	unsalted butter	1/2	tsp	freshly grated ginger (optional)
1	small	onion, chopped	Water (as needed)		
1/2	tsp	pumpkin pie spice	Plain yogurt, regular or low-fat for garnish		

Procedure

1. Preheat oven to 400°.
2. Toss squash cubes with olive oil, salt and pepper.
3. Bake on a foil-lined baking sheet for about 45 minutes until very soft, stirring halfway through.
4. Meanwhile, in a medium saucepan melt the butter and cook the onions over medium-low heat until soft, about 5 minutes. Add pumpkin pie spice and stir to combine. Add broth and ginger, if using, cover, and simmer for 10 minutes.
5. Add the roasted squash and stir well to combine.
6. Transfer mixture to a blender or food processor and puree until smooth. Add additional stock or water to achieve desired consistency. Add more salt and pepper to taste.
7. Return to the sauce pan and heat gently.
8. To serve, ladle into serving bowls, garnish with a dollop of yogurt or sour cream.

Servings: 3
Yield: about 3 cups

Preparation Time: 15 minutes
Cooking Time: 45 minutes

Nutrition Facts

Serving size: 1 cup

Cook's Notes

Amount Per Serving	
Calories	123.19
Calories From Fat (43%)	52.45
	% Daily Value
Total Fat 5.87g	9%
Saturated Fat 2.99g	15%
Cholesterol 14.98mg	5%
Sodium 232.38mg	10%
Potassium 349.13mg	10%
Total Carbohydrates 13.42g	4%
Fiber 1.37g	5%
Sugar 4.88g	
Protein 4.85g	10%

Cabbage & Tomato Főzelék ½

This is a simple, humble dish, but it's one of my childhood favorites. Unfortunately my husband is not in love with the cabbage family so this is for you cabbage lovers.

1/2	head	green cabbage, shredded	1	Tbs	flour
1	small	sweet onion, peeled and left whole	1 (15-oz)		can tomato sauce
1	tsp	salt	1	tsp	sugar (optional)
1	Tbs	olive oil	1/4	tsp	caraway seeds (optional)

Procedure

1. In a large soup pot place shredded cabbage and onion and fill pan with water to barely cover. Season with salt, cover and bring to a boil, cover and simmer until tender, 20 - 25 minutes.

2. When cabbage is tender, heat oil in a medium size skillet until shimmering. Sprinkle in flour and stir until it is blond in color. Remove from the heat and stir in tomato sauce. Whisk vigorously until smooth.

3. Pour into soup pot and stir until well combined. Taste and add a bit of sugar (if desired), salt and caraway seeds (if desired).

Servings: 4

Preparation Time: 15 minutes
Cooking Time: 30 minutes

Nutrition Facts

Serving size: 1 cup

Cook's Notes

Amount Per Serving	
Calories	85.4
Calories From Fat (37%)	31.73
	% Daily Value
Total Fat 3.6g	6%
Saturated Fat 0.49g	2%
Cholesterol 0mg	0%
Sodium 911.08mg	38%
Potassium 324.16mg	9%
Total Carbohydrates 12.79g	4%
Fiber 2.04g	8%
Sugar 8.17g	
Protein 1.84g	4%

Recipe Tips

Many Hungarian cooks use sugar but you can use a touch of Stevia in lieu of sugar. However, using a sweet onion such as Vidalia may provide enough sweetness.

Carrot Soup with O.J. & Tarragon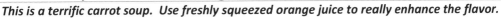

This is a terrific carrot soup. Use freshly squeezed orange juice to really enhance the flavor.

1	Tbs	unsalted butter	1/2	cup	orange juice
1	lb	carrots, peeled and sliced	1	Tbs	brandy (optional)
3/4	cup	chopped onion	2	tsp	chopped fresh tarragon
3	cups	low sodium chicken broth			Salt and pepper to taste
					Tarragon sprigs for garnish

Procedure

1 In a heavy soup pot melt butter over medium heat. Add onions and carrots and sauté until onion is soft, 5 - 8 minutes.

2 Add chicken broth, cover and bring to a boil. Reduce heat and simmer until carrots are very tender, 10 - 12 minutes.

3 Remove from heat and allow to cool slightly. Pour into a blender and purée until mixture is very smooth.

4 Return to soup pot, stir in orange juice, brandy (if using) and chopped tarragon.

5 Simmer for 5 minutes to blend flavors. Season to taste with salt and pepper. Ladle into soup bowls, garnish with tarragon sprigs and serve.

Servings: 4

Preparation Time: 15 minutes
Cooking Time: 20 minutes

Nutrition Facts

Serving size: about 1 cup

Cook's Notes

Amount Per Serving	
Calories	146.75
Calories From Fat (27%)	39.12
	% Daily Value
Total Fat 4.39g	7%
Saturated Fat 2.19g	11%
Cholesterol 7.63mg	3%
Sodium 664.35mg	28%
Potassium 781.17mg	22%
Total Carbohydrates 22.24g	7%
Fiber 5.1g	20%
Sugar 12.07g	
Protein 5.73g	11%

Recipe Tips

Using a bag of peeled baby carrots makes this a fast and easy soup to prepare.

This is from Sarah Brown and has been a favorite of ours since our vegetarian years in the mid 1980's. It is pictured on page 165.

2	Tbs	unsalted butter	1	tsp	ground cumin
1	Tbs	olive oil	4	cups	free-range, low-sodium chicken
12	oz	baby carrots, peeled and sliced			broth
3		celery stalks, diced	Salt and pepper to taste		
2	tsp	ground coriander	1	Tbs	chopped fresh cilantro

Procedure

1 In a medium-size saucepan, melt butter and olive oil over medium heat. Add carrots and celery and sauté for about 5 minutes, stirring to coat evenly.

2 Add the ground coriander and cumin and sauté for another 3 - 4 minutes to release their flavor.

3 Pour in the broth and bring to a boil. Cover and turn the heat to low. Simmer for about 30 minutes or until the vegetables are tender. Allow to cool slightly.

4 Pour into a blender and process until smooth. Return to a clean saucepan. Season to taste with salt and pepper and reheat gently.

5 Ladle into serving bowls, sprinkle with chopped cilantro and serve.

Servings: 6

Preparation Time: 15 minutes
Cooking Time: 30 minutes

Nutrition Facts

Serving size: 1 cup

Cook's Notes

Amount Per Serving	
Calories	97.3
Calories From Fat (62%)	60.33
	% Daily Value
Total Fat 6.79g	10%
Saturated Fat 2.78g	14%
Cholesterol 10.18mg	3%
Sodium 135.59mg	6%
Potassium 259.04mg	7%
Total Carbohydrates 7.96g	3%
Fiber 2.26g	9%
Sugar 3.11g	
Protein 1.54g	3%

According to my mother, my uncle coined the phrase of "rag soup" when he was just a boy because the eggs look like rags floating in the soup.

1 large	egg, lightly beaten		2 cups	low sodium chicken broth
1 tsp	chopped fresh parsley		1 cup	baby spinach
Freshly ground nutmeg			Salt and freshly ground black pepper to taste	
2 Tbs	grated Parmigiano-Reggiano cheese, and more for garnish			

Procedure

1 In a small bowl whisk eggs, parsley and freshly ground nutmeg. Stir in 1 tablespoon of cheese.

2 In a medium-size saucepan on moderate heat, bring chicken broth to a boil. Vigorously whisk in the egg mixture, stir in spinach and reduce heat to low. Cover and simmer for 1 minute until spinach wilts.

3 Remove from heat and season with salt and pepper. Ladle into bowls and sprinkle with remainder of cheese.

Servings: 2

Preparation Time: 5 minutes
Cooking Time: 20 minutes

Nutrition Facts

Serving size: about 1 cup

Cook's Notes

Amount Per Serving	
Calories	81.7
Calories From Fat (49%)	40.38
	% Daily Value
Total Fat 4.42g	7%
Saturated Fat 1.69g	8%
Cholesterol 97.4mg	32%
Sodium 239.18mg	10%
Potassium 128.44mg	4%
Total Carbohydrates 3.04g	1%
Fiber 0.38g	2%
Sugar 0.25g	
Protein 6.52g	13%

My original recipe uses freshly squeezed lemon juice but it was too tart for my husband's throat. The lemon flax oil adds the lemon flavor but none of the tartness.

3		avocados, preferably Hass, peeled and cut into 1/2-inch dice	1	tsp	salt
			2	Tbs	chopped fresh cilantro more for garnish
1/4	cup	sliced scallions	1	cup	heavy (whipping) cream
1 1/2	cups	free range chicken broth			
1	Tbs	flax oil with lemon			

Procedure

1 Puree avocados, scallions, broth, flax oil, salt and cilantro. Chill directly in the pitcher of the blender.

2 Just before serving stir in the cream. Taste and add more salt and chicken stock for desired flavor and consistency. Serve chilled garnished with a little cilantro.

Servings: 4

Preparation Time: 10 minutes

Nutrition Facts

Serving size: about 1 cup

Cook's Notes

Amount Per Serving	
Calories	461.87
Calories From Fat (85%)	393.38
	% Daily Value
Total Fat 45.6g	70%
Saturated Fat 16.93g	85%
Cholesterol 81.52mg	27%
Sodium 659.85mg	27%
Potassium 732.1mg	21%
Total Carbohydrates 14.18g	5%
Fiber 9.05g	36%
Sugar 0.6g	
Protein 4.3g	9%

My sister and I collaborated on this recipe. It is very refreshing on a warm summer day.

2 pints	fresh blueberries reserving a few for garnish	2	cardamom pods	
2 cups	water	2 Tbs	agave nectar	
1 whole	cinnamon stick	1 Tbs	grated fresh ginger root	
		1 cup	plain Greek-style yogurt, reserving a bit for garnish	

Procedure

1 In a large saucepan combine blueberries, water, cinnamon stick, cardamom pods, agave and fresh ginger. Bring to a boil, reduce heat, and simmer, stirring occasionally until blueberries burst, about 8 minutes. Remove cinnamon stick and cardamom pods. Allow to cool for a few minutes.

2 Purée in batches (if necessary) in blender until smooth.

3 Place a chinoise (or fine-mesh strainer) over a clean saucepan and strain out solids, discarding them. Cover and chill for several hours or overnight.

4 Just before serving whisk in yogurt. Garnish with reserved yogurt and whole blueberries.

Servings: 6

Preparation Time: 10 minutes
Cooking Time: 20 minutes

Nutrition Facts

Serving size: about 1 cup

Cook's Notes

Amount Per Serving	
Calories	64.49
Calories From Fat (12%)	7.51
	% Daily Value
Total Fat 0.87g	1%
Saturated Fat 0.41g	2%
Cholesterol 2.31mg	<1%
Sodium 30.26mg	1%
Potassium 138.07mg	4%
Total Carbohydrates 13.23g	4%
Fiber 2.6g	10%
Sugar 5.95g	
Protein 2.52g	5%

This recipe is from Tom McCann's in Sedan, Kansas. He and his lovely wife Janet are the restaurant owners and this is one of Tom's creations.

1 1/2	cups	heavy (whipping) cream
2	Tbs	fresh lime juice
4	medium	cucumbers, peeled, seeded and cut into tiny cubes
1 1/2	cups	1/4-inch diced celery
1/2	cup	thinly sliced scallions (white part and tips of green part)

1/2	cup	free range, low sodium chicken broth
1	tsp	salt
2	tsp	dried dill weed
1/2	tsp	freshly ground black pepper
2	cups	sour cream or plain yogurt

Scallion greens, fresh dill or sour cream for garnish

Procedure

1 In a large bowl combine heavy cream and cucumbers. Set aside.

2 In a food processor fitted with a metal blade, add remaining ingredients and pulse to a fine mince. Add to cucumber mixture, stir to combine well and chill until very cold, at least 3 hours.

3 Serve garnished with additional scallion greens, snipped fresh dill or a dollop of sour cream.

Servings: 6

Preparation Time: 15 minutes

Nutrition Facts

Serving size: 1 generous cup

Cook's Notes

Amount Per Serving	
Calories	185.12
Calories From Fat (60%)	111.4
	% Daily Value
Total Fat 12.67g	19%
Saturated Fat 7.74g	39%
Cholesterol 45.83mg	15%
Sodium 494.53mg	21%
Potassium 515.24mg	15%
Total Carbohydrates 12.54g	4%
Fiber 1.77g	7%
Sugar 8.85g	
Protein 6.24g	12%

I often make this for myself because it is so delicious and I love to give it a little kick by using spicy tomatoes. Substitute plain diced tomatoes for the swallowing impaired.

2 cups	chicken broth		1 cup	frozen corn
1 (15-oz)	can refried beans		1 (10 oz)	can Rotel tomatoes
1 (15-oz)	can black beans, rinsed and drained		Chopped cilantro, shredded cheddar, sour cream, chopped avocado and chives for garnish	

Procedure

1 In a medium-size sauce pan whisk together chicken broth and refried beans until smooth.

2 Add remaining ingredients and heat while stirring occasionally until bubbly, about 15 minutes.

3 Serve with garnish toppings.

Servings: 6

Preparation Time: 10 minutes
Cooking Time: 15 minutes

Nutrition Facts

Serving size: about 1 cup

Cook's Notes

Amount Per Serving	
Calories	110.42
Calories From Fat (8%)	9.13
	% Daily Value
Total Fat 1.01g	2%
Saturated Fat 0.22g	1%
Cholesterol 0mg	0%
Sodium 568mg	24%
Potassium 356.82mg	10%
Total Carbohydrates 20.61g	7%
Fiber 5.18g	21%
Sugar 1.03g	
Protein 6.09g	12%

179

Potatoes and Parsnips make an awesome duo in this hearty soup.

6	parsnips, peeled and cut into 1/2" dice	2 fresh		bay leaves
4 large	russet potatoes, peeled and cut into 1/2" cubes	1 1/2	inch	piece of fresh ginger, freshly grated
Salt to taste		1/2	tsp	white pepper, or to taste
2 slices	bacon, diced	2	Tbs	white wine vinegar
1 large	onion, finely chopped	1	Tbs	light brown sugar (or sucanat)
1 small	celery stalk, finely chopped	1	quart	free range chicken broth
1 sprig	fresh thyme	1/4	cup	minced fresh parsley

Procedure

1 In a medium-size saucepan cover parsnips and potatoes with water, add salt and bring to a boil. Cook until very tender, about 20 minutes. Drain and mash with a potato masher.

2 Combine olive oil and bacon in a large soup pot and cook on medium heat until brown, about 8 minutes. Add onions, celery, thyme sprig, bay leaves, ginger, a little white pepper, vinegar, and brown sugar (or sucanat) and cook until very soft.

3 Add mashed parsnips and potatoes to pot and stir to combine with chicken broth, adding water to thin if soup is too thick. Adjust salt and pepper to taste and stir in parsley.

Servings: 8

Preparation Time: 30 minutes
Cooking Time: 30 minutes

Nutrition Facts

Serving size: 1 ¼ cups

Cook's Notes

Amount Per Serving	
Calories	295.44
Calories From Fat (15%)	44.77
	% Daily Value
Total Fat 5g	8%
Saturated Fat 1.54g	8%
Cholesterol 6.46mg	2%
Sodium 416.77mg	17%
Potassium 1393.5mg	40%
Total Carbohydrates 59.62g	20%
Fiber 11.7g	47%
Sugar 12.2g	
Protein 5.97g	12%

Recipe Tips

For a smoother soup, purée in a blender, then garnish with parsley.

I love this hearty soup, inspired by Rachael Ray. Using quinoa flakes makes the meatballs so tender they practically melt in your mouth.

1	bunch	broccoli rabe, washed, with stems cut 1" below florets
1/2	lb	ground pork
1 1/2	tsp	fennel seeds
1/2	tsp	smoked paprika
6		garlic cloves, finely chopped, divided
1/4	cup	quinoa flakes
1	large	egg
Salt and pepper to taste		
1/2	cup	grated Parmigiano-Reggiano cheese and more for serving
2	Tbs	olive oil

1/4	lb	pancetta, diced
1	large	sweet onion, chopped
1	head	escarole, washed and roughly chopped
Freshly grated nutmeg		
1 (14 oz)		can cannellini beans, rinsed and drained
4 cups		free range chicken broth
2 cups		water
1 cup		orzo, ditalini or other small pasta shape, uncooked

Procedure

1 In a large pot of boiling salted water, blanch broccoli rabe for 5 minutes. Drain and drop into an ice bath. Set aside. Cook the orzo or other pasta according to package directions or until soft. Drain and set aside.

2 In a medium-size bowl mix pork with fennel seeds, paprika, 2 cloves of garlic, quinoa flakes, egg, salt, pepper, and grated cheese. Mix until well combined.

3 In a large soup pot heat olive oil over medium high heat. Add pancetta and brown, stirring, 3 - 4 minutes. Add onions, remaining garlic and sauté for 5 minutes. Stir in escarole, season with salt and pepper and freshly grated nutmeg. Add broth and water and bring to a low boil.

4 Using a small ice cream scoop or melon baller, carefully drop little meatballs into simmering soup. Cook about 5 minutes then add beans, broccoli rabe and adjust seasoning.

5 To serve, put a little cooked orzo or pasta in the bottom of a soup bowl and ladle the soup on top. Sprinkle with additional cheese and serve.

Servings: 6
Preparation Time: 30 minutes
Cooking Time: 15 minutes

Nutrition Facts

Serving size: 1 ½ cups

Cook's Notes

Amount Per Serving	
Calories	444.48
Calories From Fat (51%)	227.07
	% Daily Value
Total Fat 25.35g	39%
Saturated Fat 8.23g	41%
Cholesterol 77.92mg	26%
Sodium 404.7mg	17%
Potassium 734.08mg	21%
Total Carbohydrates 33.15g	11%
Fiber 6.57g	26%
Sugar 1.74g	
Protein 22.32g	45%

Onion Soup

The transformation of the humble onion is a standard fare in bistros in France but it is a very common offering in the US also. I like using onions such as Vidalia or Maui, which have their own sweetness and depth of flavor. I use a food processor to pulse the onions rather than the traditional slicing method. Using croutons rather than a slice of bread floating in the soup, as well as reducing the amount of cheese makes for much easier swallowing.

1	Tbs	unsalted butter
1	Tbs	extra-virgin olive oil
2	large	sweet onions, chopped
2	large	garlic cloves, finely chopped
1		bay leaf
2	small	sprigs of thyme
1/2	tsp	salt

Freshly ground black pepper to taste

1/2	cup	dry white wine
1	Tbs	brandy, (optional)
1	Tbs	flour
1	quart	low sodium beef broth
4	slices	French bread, crusts removed and cubed
1/4	cup	grated Swiss cheese

Fresh snipped chives for garnish (optional)

Procedure

1. In a large heavy soup pot heat butter and oil over medium high heat. Add onions, garlic, bay leaf, thyme sprigs, salt and pepper and sauté until onions are very soft and caramelized, 25 - 30 minutes.
2. Add the wine and brandy (if using), bring to a boil, reduce heat and simmer until liquid is reduced and onions are dry, 3 - 5 minutes. Discard bay leaf and thyme sprigs.
3. Sprinkle in the flour and stir to combine. Cook on low heat stirring to remove the starchiness of the flour, about 5 minutes.
4. Stir in the broth and bring to a simmer. Cook over medium low heat, about 10 minutes. Season to taste with salt and pepper. Turn off heat and cover while preparing croutons.
5. Preheat an over broiler. Arrange bread cubes on a baking sheet in a single layer. Lightly toast bread cubes on both sides until golden brown, about 5 minutes. Remove and set aside.
6. When ready to serve, ladle soup into bowls set on a sheet tray. Float a few croutons in the center of soup, sprinkle with cheese and broil until cheese melts and is bubbly, 3 - 5 minutes. Garnish with snipped chives, if desired.

Servings: 4

Preparation Time: 10 minutes   Cooking Time: 45 minutes

Nutrition Facts

Serving size: about 1 cup

Cook's Notes

Amount Per Serving	
Calories	271.11
Calories From Fat (31%)	83.34
	% Daily Value
Total Fat 9.43g	15%
Saturated Fat 3.92g	20%
Cholesterol 15.22mg	5%
Sodium 459.26mg	19%
Potassium 276.79mg	8%
Total Carbohydrates 34.38g	11%
Fiber 2.41g	10%
Sugar 9.54g	
Protein 7.93g	16%

This incredible soup came from Paula Deen who finishes the soup with champagne but we like it without the bubbly.

4	oz	unsalted butter	2	cups	heavy (whipping) cream
1	large	shallot or 1 small yellow onion, finely diced (about 1/2 cup)	3/4	lb	brie cheese, rind removed and cut into pieces
1/4	cup	all-purpose flour	1	small	bunch chives, snipped
2	cups	clam juice			Salt and pepper to taste
1 1/2	cups	free range, low-sodium chicken broth	2		dozen fresh oysters, shucked

Procedure

1. In a heavy saucepan melt butter over low heat. Add shallots and sauté until softened, about 5 minutes.
2. Sprinkle in flour and cook until lightly colored, about 1 minute.
3. Gradually whisk in the clam juice, chicken broth and cream.
4. Increase heat to medium-high and bring to a boil; reduce heat to low and simmer for 10 minutes.
5. Add the brie, chives, salt and pepper to taste and stir until cheese is melted. Add the oysters and cook for 3 minutes.
6. Serve with snipped chives for garnish.

Servings: 6

Preparation Time: 30 minutes
Cooking Time: 20 minutes

Nutrition Facts

Serving size: about 1 cup

Cook's Notes

Amount Per Serving	
Calories	910.58
Calories From Fat (89%)	810.41
	% Daily Value
Total Fat 92.12g	142%
Saturated Fat 57.84g	289%
Cholesterol 281.57mg	94%
Sodium 992.84mg	41%
Potassium 183.72mg	5%
Total Carbohydrates 8.12g	3%
Fiber 0.19g	<1%
Sugar 0.7g	
Protein 15.7g	31%

Pea & Parsnip Soup

This has a very natural sweet flavor.

1	small	shallot, finely diced	1		bay leaf
2	cups	frozen green peas	Salt and pepper to taste		
3	cups	chicken broth	2	Tbs	snipped fresh dill
1/2	cup	1/2" diced peeled parsnips	Sour cream or plain yogurt for garnish		

Procedure

1 Place all ingredients except dill into a saucepan. Bring to a boil, reduce heat and simmer for about 15 minutes, until parsnips and peas are tender.

2 Add salt and pepper to taste. Allow to cool slightly and puree in a blender.

3 Return to the saucepan and add dill. Serve with a dollop of sour cream or yogurt.

Servings: 4

Preparation Time: 10 minutes
Cooking Time: 20 minutes

Nutrition Facts

Serving size: about 1 cup

Cook's Notes

Amount Per Serving	
Calories	94.88
Calories From Fat (12%)	11.28
	% Daily Value
Total Fat 1.41g	2%
Saturated Fat 0.38g	2%
Cholesterol 0mg	0%
Sodium 128.5mg	5%
Potassium 330.22mg	9%
Total Carbohydrates 14.74g	5%
Fiber 3.84g	15%
Sugar 4.38g	
Protein 7.37g	15%

Plantain Soup

I had never used plantains before watching Ingrid Hoffman on one of the cooking channels. This version is hearty and lip-smacking.

1	Tbs	olive oil
1	small	yellow onion, finely chopped
1	medium	carrot ,peeled and diced
1	medium	celery stalk, diced
2		garlic cloves, finely chopped
1/2	tsp	ground cumin

4 1/2	cups	chicken broth
2	green	plantains, peeled and thinly sliced
2	large	bay leaves
1 1/2	small	zucchini, thinly sliced
1	cup	chopped fresh cilantro
Salt and freshly ground pepper to taste		

Procedure

1. In a medium-size sauce pan heat olive oil on medium-high heat. Add onions, carrots, celery, and garlic and cook until onions are soft, about 8 minutes. Sprinkle in the cumin and sauté for about 30 seconds.
2. Add chicken broth, plantains, and bay leaves, cover and bring to a boil. Reduce heat to lowest heat and barely simmer, uncovered, until the plantains are very tender, about 45 minutes.
3. Add zucchini and cilantro during the last 10 minutes of simmering. Remove from heat and allow to cool a bit. Remove bay leaves.
4. Transfer half of the soup to a blender and puree until smooth. Stir the puree back into the pot and mix well.
5. If the soup is too thick add more chicken broth or water.
6. Season with salt and pepper to taste. Serve warm.

Servings: 6

Preparation Time: 20 minutes
Cooking Time: 45 minutes

Nutrition Facts

Serving size: about ¼ cup

Amount Per Serving	
Calories	164.04
Calories From Fat (26%)	43.29
	% Daily Value
Total Fat 4.82g	7%
Saturated Fat 1g	5%
Cholesterol 5.4mg	2%
Sodium 279.87mg	12%
Potassium 627.72mg	18%
Total Carbohydrates 26.06g	9%
Fiber 2.3g	9%
Sugar 12.11g	
Protein 6.06g	12%

Potato Főzelék

This is a simple and delicious Főzelék. It's not quite as yummy as my aunt Ica used to make but it reminds me of her when I make it.

2 large	baking potatoes, peeled and cut into 1" cubes	1/4	tsp	freshly ground black pepper
1 small	onion, chopped	2	Tbs	corn starch (or arrowroot)
1	fresh bay leaf	1/3	cup	sour cream or plain yogurt
1 tsp	salt	1	Tbs	fresh lemon juice or vinegar

Procedure

1. In a medium-size sauce pan, add potatoes, onion, bay leaf and salt and pepper. Add water to cover and bring to a boil. Simmer until tender, 15 - 20 minutes.
2. In a small bowl mix corn starch with sour cream (or yogurt) until smooth. Bring potatoes back to a low boil and stir in sour cream mixture, stirring until thickened.
3. Remove from heat, taste and season with additional salt and pepper if necessary. Add lemon juice (or vinegar) to taste. (It should be mildly tart.)

Servings: 2

Preparation Time: 10 minutes
Cooking Time: 25 minutes

Nutrition Facts

Serving size: about 1 cup

Cook's Notes

Amount Per Serving	
Calories	247.65
Calories From Fat (3%)	6.78
	% Daily Value
Total Fat 0.78g	1%
Saturated Fat 0.45g	2%
Cholesterol 2.45mg	<1%
Sodium 1204.71mg	50%
Potassium 1335.26mg	38%
Total Carbohydrates 55.99g	19%
Fiber 4.05g	16%
Sugar 5.95g	
Protein 6.91g	14%

Roasted Borscht ½

Roasting beets brings out their fabulous sweet flavor. In the winter I just roast them with olive oil and fresh thyme and serve it as a side dish. We can thank Tyler Florence for this idea.

1	lb	raw beets (about 3)	4	cups	chicken broth
Salt and pepper to taste			2	Tbs	red wine vinegar
6		thyme sprigs	1	Tbs	honey or maple syrup
4	Tbs	olive oil	1	medium	Granny Smith apple, peeled, cored, and grated
1	medium	onion, chopped			
2	medium	carrots, peeled and chopped	2	Tbs	chopped fresh dill sprigs
2		garlic cloves, chopped	1/2	cup	sour cream

Procedure

1. Preheat oven to 400°.
2. Cut off green stems and scrub beets and place them in a large piece of aluminum foil. Season with salt and pepper, add 3 thyme sprigs and drizzle with 3 Tbs. olive oil. Close foil tightly and bake until beets are tender, about 1 hour. Set aside. When beets are cool enough to handle, slip off their skins and chop into large chunks. (Might want to use rubber gloves because beets can stain the hands.)
3. In a large heavy pot over medium heat add remaining olive oil. Sauté onion, carrots and garlic and 3 remaining thyme sprigs until vegetables are tender, about 20 minutes. Remove thyme sprigs.
4. Place chunks of beets into a blender, add cooked vegetables and enough of the broth to make a smooth consistency. Add the vinegar and honey (or maple syrup) and season with additional salt and pepper to taste.
5. Serve warm or cold. Garnish with grated apples, sour cream and dill.

Servings: 8

Preparation Time: 30 minutes
Cooking Time: 1 hour and 30 minutes

Nutrition Facts

Serving size: 1 generous cup

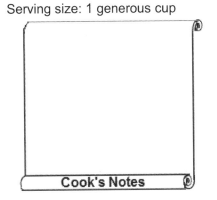

Cook's Notes

Amount Per Serving	
Calories	191.77
Calories From Fat (52%)	99.75
	% Daily Value
Total Fat 11.25g	17%
Saturated Fat 3.01g	15%
Cholesterol 11.08mg	4%
Sodium 250.76mg	10%
Potassium 477.99mg	14%
Total Carbohydrates 19.04g	6%
Fiber 3.03g	12%
Sugar 12.11g	
Protein 4.82g	10%

Tomato & Bean Soup

Giada De Laurentiis gave me the idea for this soup. Using crushed tomatoes makes it easier.

2	Tbs	unsalted butter	1		bay leaf
1	medium	onion, chopped	1	sprig	fresh rosemary, plus 1
2	medium	carrots, peeled and chopped			teaspoon minced
2	medium	garlic cloves, chopped	3/4	tsp	salt
1	(15-oz)	can white beans, drained and	1/2	tsp	freshly ground black pepper
		rinsed	2/3	cup	sour cream
1	(28 oz)	can crushed tomatoes	1		lemon, zested
3	cups	free range, low-sodium chicken			
		broth			

Procedure

1. In a large soup pot melt butter over medium high heat. Add onions, carrots and garlic and sauté until vegetables are tender, about 5 minutes.
2. Add beans, tomatoes, broth, bay leaf and rosemary sprig. Cover, bring soup to a boil, reduce heat to low and simmer 30 minutes.
3. Remove rosemary sprig and bay leaf. Using an immersion blender, purée soup to desired consistency. Season with the salt and freshly ground pepper to taste.
4. In a medium bowl, fold lemon zest into sour cream, and add minced rosemary. Mix well.
5. Ladle soup into serving bowls and add a dollop of lemon rosemary scented sour cream to the center of each bowl of soup.

Servings: 6

Preparation Time: 10 minutes
Cooking Time: 35 minutes

Nutrition Facts

Serving size: about 1 cup

Cook's Notes

Amount Per Serving	
Calories	250.62
Calories From Fat (34%)	85.92
	% Daily Value
Total Fat 9.74g	15%
Saturated Fat 5.51g	28%
Cholesterol 23.47mg	8%
Sodium 493.23mg	21%
Potassium 984.29mg	28%
Total Carbohydrates 32.47g	11%
Fiber 7.82g	31%
Sugar 3.01g	
Protein 10.72g	21%

We love kale but you can certainly use spinach or other greens if you prefer.

2	Tbs	olive oil	3/4	tsp	salt
1	small	red onion, thinly sliced	1/4	tsp	freshly ground black pepper
2	cloves	garlic, chopped			
1		bay leaf	2 (15-oz)		cans white beans, drained and rinsed
1 1/2	lb	kale, rinsed and roughly chopped	1 (14.5 oz)		can diced tomatoes, drained
			1/2	cup	free-range chicken broth

Procedure

1. In a large skillet heat olive oil over medium-high heat. Add onions, garlic and bay leaf and sauté until onions are soft, 3 - 4 minutes.
2. Add kale, salt and pepper and cook for another 2 minutes.
3. Add beans, tomatoes and broth.
4. Cover and cook on low heat until kale is wilted and cooked through, about 15 minutes. Taste and adjust seasonings before serving.

Servings: 4

Preparation Time: 15 minutes
Cooking Time: 30 minutes

Nutrition Facts

Serving size: about 1 cup

Cook's Notes

Amount Per Serving	
Calories	492.15
Calories From Fat (16%)	77.39
	% Daily Value
Total Fat 8.81g	14%
Saturated Fat 1.34g	7%
Cholesterol 0mg	0%
Sodium 1050.34mg	44%
Potassium 2564.2mg	73%
Total Carbohydrates 80.51g	27%
Fiber 21.2g	85%
Sugar 2.23g	
Protein 29.54g	59%

Zucchini Squash Főzelék

You can make this with zucchini, yellow squash or a combination of both.

1	Tbs	butter
1	small	onion, finely chopped
2	large	zucchini or yellow squash, grated
1	tsp	salt

1/2	cup	plain Greek-style yogurt
1 1/2	Tbs	chopped fresh dill
1	tsp	fresh lemon juice
		Lemon zest (optional)
1/4	tsp	paprika for garnish, (optional)

Procedure

1 In a medium-size saucepan on medium heat, melt butter. Sauté onions until translucent, about 5 minutes.

2 Add zucchini, season with salt and continue to cook until zucchini is tender, about 5 minutes.

3 Stir dill into yogurt and add to zucchini. Add lemon juice (and zest if desired). Stir to combine.

4 Sprinkle top with paprika to garnish, if using, and serve.

Servings: 2

Preparation Time: 15 minutes
Cooking Time: 15 minutes

Nutrition Facts

Serving size: about 1 cup

Cook's Notes

Amount Per Serving	
Calories	162.48
Calories From Fat (48%)	77.99
	% Daily Value
Total Fat 8.92g	14%
Saturated Fat 5.23g	26%
Cholesterol 23.23mg	8%
Sodium 1219.41mg	51%
Potassium 1022.56mg	29%
Total Carbohydrates 17.89g	6%
Fiber 3.93g	16%
Sugar 12.96g	
Protein 6.58g	13%

T his is a list and description of some recipe ingredients you may not be familiar with.

Artificial Sweeteners

These are never a healthy alternative. They are toxic and should be avoided. A few examples are Aspartame, Saccharin, and Sucralose.

Agave Syrup

Is a sweetener commercially produced in South Africa and Mexico from several species of agave, including the Blue Agave (used to make tequila). Agave nectar is sweeter than honey, though less viscous. Let its taste be your guide when using it in recipes that call for honey or maple syrup.

Arame

Is a sea vegetable (seaweed) used in Japanese dishes, high in calcium, iodine, iron, magnesium and other minerals. It is sold dry and needs to be soaked in water. Follow the recipe provided in the *"Salads & Dressings"* section or use the instructions on the back of the package.

Arrowroot

Arrowroot thickens at a lower temperature than cornstarch and is not weakened by acidic ingredients, has a more neutral taste, and is not affected by freezing. However it doesn't mix well with dairy. Mix arrowroot with a cool liquid (like water or fruit juice) before adding to a hot liquid.

Birch Sugar

It is derived from the birch tree bark but the trees are not cut down. It is also known as Xylitol and only has half the calories of sugar which makes it ideal for baking. It dissolves quickly and looks and tastes like sugar with no unpleasant after taste.

Buckwheat Groats

It is commonly used in Eastern Europe, especially Russia, and Western Asia. It is also called kasha and is often considered a peasant dish. You may have heard of Kasha Varnishkes.

Cardamom Pods

They are small seed pods, triangular-shaped with a thin papery outer shell and small black seeds inside. It is the third most expensive spice, after saffron and vanilla. It also comes in ground form. I use the pods and remove them before serving. It is commonly used in Indian cooking.

Capers

The flower buds of the caper bush and are used as a seasoning or garnish. They are used in Italian and Mediterranean dishes. The flavor is intense and only a small amount is required to add a sharp flavor to any sauce or dish.

Date Palm Sugar (Coconut Palm Sugar)

They both resemble brown sugar in looks but don't have the metallic flavor of brown sugar. In cooking they have a very low melting point. This makes it a suitable sweetener to use, especially in baking. Although the names are used interchangeably palm sugar and coconut sugar are not the same. One comes from the date palm (also called sugar palm) and the other from the coconut palm, but both are produced from the sweet, watery sap from cut flower buds or from the sap of the tree. Both are lower on the glycemic index than table sugar meaning they impact blood glucose elevation in a lesser and healthier way.

Flax Seeds (Ground Meal)

The seeds have a slightly nutty flavor and an abundance of omega-3 fatty acids. Whole and ground flaxseeds, as well as flaxseed oil, are available. The seeds are slightly larger than sesame seeds and have a hard, smooth shiny shell. They come in reddish brown or golden amber, depending on variety. The nutrients in ground flax seeds are more easily absorbed, making them ideal to include in smoothies or on cereals.

Garam Masala

It is a blend of ground spices used in Indian and other South Asian recipes. It can be used alone or with other spices and seasonings. It is pungent but not hot.

Just Like Sugar®

It is a blend of chicory root, dietary fiber, Vitamin C, calcium and the flavor from orange peels. The granules are as sweet as sugar and can be used in cooking and baking.

Maple Syrup

It is made from sap collected from mature maple trees. It is refined and processed but more nutritious than refined white table sugar.

Oils

Canola Oil - Because of its light flavor it is versatile for cooking. Use it for sautéing, stir-frying, grilling and baking. Add it to salad dressings, sauce or marinades anytime you need a neutral taste.

Coconut Oil - Extracted from the kernel or flesh of the mature coconut palm and is very heat stable, which makes it suitable for cooking at high temperatures.

Extra Virgin Olive - First pressing of ripe olives. This is my #1 choice for cooking.

Flax Oil - Also known as linseed oil and is obtained by cold pressing. It is not suitable for cooking but is great in smoothies and for drizzling as finishing oil. It comes in flavors such as cinnamon, pomegranate, and lemon.

Peanut Oil - A mild tasting vegetable oil derived from peanuts. It has a high smoke point and is ideal for higher temperatures.

Panko

Is Japanese-style bread crumbs. It is made from bread without the crust and is coarsely ground into large flakes for a crunchy coating. They stay crisp longer than breadcrumbs because they do not absorb as much fat or liquid.

Quinoa Grain, Flakes & Flour

A rediscovered ancient "grain" native to South America, quinoa was once called "the gold of the Incas." Not only is quinoa high in protein, but it is a complete protein, in that that it contains all nine essential amino acids. Quinoa is high in lysine which is essential for tissue growth and repair. It cooks up much like rice or other grains. The flakes (usually found in the cereal aisle) make a great hot breakfast. It works well in some recipes as a replacement for bread crumbs. The flour is wonderful in baked goods.

Star Anise

Is a star-shaped pod of an evergreen tree having a licorice or anise flavor. Star anise is available in packages in Asian supermarkets. When purchasing look for whole pieces that aren't broken.

Stevia

Is a zero calorie sweetener commonly known as sweet leaf, or simply stevia. It is used as a sweetener and sugar substitute, and works quite well in hot drinks, coffee, tea, and smoothies. It is labeled as a dietary supplement because it was banned in the US in the 1990's. It does not have the same properties as sugar for baking, but because of its negligible effects on blood glucose levels and because it is a natural sweetener, it is a great alternative for refined white sugar. It comes in various forms such as a powder, individual packets, or flavored drops.

Sucanat

Is the brand name of pure, dried sugar cane juice used in place of brown sugar. Unlike traditional brown sugar, vitamins, minerals, and molasses are not lost during the processing.

Tahini

Tahini, or sesame paste, is made of hulled, lightly roasted ground sesame seeds. It is a major component of hummus (chickpeas with tahini) and other Greek, Turkish, and Middle Eastern foods.

Tamari Soy Sauce/Shōyu

Is a condiment produced by fermenting soybeans. Shōyu is traditionally divided into five main categories depending on differences in their ingredients and method of production. Most, but not all Japanese soy sauces include wheat as a primary ingredient but there are many brands that are wheat-free. Be sure to check the label to be certain.

Tofu

Tofu, also called bean curd, is a food made by coagulating soy milk then pressing the curds into soft white blocks. It comes in many densities and has a low calorie count, relatively large amounts of protein and little fat. I use it sparingly but it is easy to swallow and provides a good source of protein.

Truvía®

This is a stevia-based sugar alternative. It is a natural calorie-free sweetener made by steeping the stevia leaves in water, similar to making tea. It is suitable for people with diabetes.

Umeboshi Vinegar

This vinegar, made from Japanese-style traditional pickle plum (which is really more like an apricot) is considered good for digestion, for the prevention of nausea, and for toxicity problems, including hangovers. Its citric acid is claimed to act as an antibacterial that helps to increase saliva production and assists in the digestion of rice. It is very salty and sour. It comes in the "plum" form, as a paste as well as vinegar.

Xylitol

Is a natural sugar substitute with a very low glycemic index. One teaspoon (5 g) has 9.6 calories compared to sugar which has 15. Because it reacts similarly to heat, it can substitute for sugar in cooking and baking on an equal basis.

ZSweet® Powdered

A natural sweetener made with Erythritol, Stevia rebaudiana leaf extract and natural flavors. It measures cup for cup like powdered sugar and can be used for frosting and other baked goods. This is a zero calorie sweetener and does not promote tooth decay.

Ok, so I'm appliance, equipment and gadget happy. The listed items are definitely not *all essential* but it is important to read each recipe thoroughly first to ensure that you have or can simulate the equipment needed. Each recipe has a graphic picture of the equipment used to prepare the recipe.

Blender - Mini Blender - Magic Bullet®

It is an invaluable tool for aiding in the swallowing process. It makes everything super smooth in seconds. Depending on how much quantity I'm making I alternate between the Magic Bullet the Mini Blender or the full-size blender. The Magic Bullet is great for one serving and the blender jar is also the glass to drink from. Plastic tops come with it so it can be stored in the refrigerator or taken in the car.

Digital Scale

Use a digital scale that measures grams, ounces, and milliliters and has a tare function; get one that is flat and easy to clean.

Egg Slicer

The one I have wedges and slices and it is very compact for easy storage. I sometimes use it for mushrooms too.

Electric Kettle

I resisted buying one for a long time because I didn't want to chew up counter space but it is so handy. It not only boils water incredibly fast but it shuts itself off just in case…

Fish Spatula

This makes it easy to flip delicate fish. It can be used for delicate vegetables and because it is slotted, it drains excess fat back into the pan.

Food Processor

Couldn't live without this fantastic multi-purpose machine! The Cuisinart I am currently using dates back to the 1980's and it's still going strong. The small one I have is great for smaller jobs; I keep it on my counter.

Hand-Held Mixer

It is essential for baking and for whipping cream. My cooking expertise does not extend into the world of baking. At Le Cordon Bleu all my grades were "A's", except in baking where I was presented with my first and only "B" by our French pastry chef.

Hand-Held Grater – Box Grater

The box grater has 4 sides. The hand-held come in different sizes. All make quick and easy work out of mincing fresh garlic, grating ginger or hard-boiled eggs, etc. These old-fashioned graters are a great tool for smaller jobs. For large jobs I use my food processor.

Immersion Blender

It is wonderful for pureeing directly in the pot. You can control the amount of texture by blending as much or as little as you like. For completely smooth things, use a blender.

Juice Extractor

Centrifugal Juicers are the most popular and the most affordable. They are great at juicing most any fruit or vegetables. I have a Breville with a large feed tube, meaning that the item to be juiced doesn't have to be cut into small pieces before juicing it. The centrifugal force pushes the pulp against a strainer screen by spinning it at a very high speed. The pulp is then collected in a container and may be discarded.

Lemon/Lime Press

This is a marvelous thing. The citrus is practically turned inside out; it leaves the seeds behind and squeezes out every drop of juice.

  ✓ ***Tip*** *If the lemon or lime is hard and feels like you won't get much juice, place it in the microwave for about 10 seconds and it should release more juice for you.*

Mandoline – Slicer

Mine is a Börner model but there are many good ones out there at various price points. I like each of the blades that it comes with and it is terrific for small jobs. I suggest one that has foldable legs for stability.

Measuring Cups & Spoons

For measuring cups I like OXO good grips because the angled surface lets you read the measurement by looking straight down into the cup so you don't have to lean over to see it. The handle is soft and has a firm grip. For measuring spoons the magnetic ones that nest together are very good and store better than the ones that come on a ring.

Microplane-Zester

Terrific for citrus fruits and is indispensable for adding the flavor of the zest without that pithy bitter stuff.

Muffin Tins

This is very useful and not just for muffins – you can make pop overs in them and mini quiches. While you're at it invest in a mini muffin tin as well – they're great for making 'hors du oeuvres'.

Pie Plate

I have a deep-dish ceramic one. They're excellent for baking many things besides dessert pies. Recently I also invested in a pie ring to keep the crust from getting too brown before the inside fully cooks.

Ring Mold Set

Not essential, but a set of pastry cutters with their various sizes makes a pretty presentation, especially if you try my green "bread" pictured on the back cover, recipe (page 19).

Silpat – Silicone Liners

Originally made in France of fiberglass and silicone to which nothing sticks. Not essential but worth the investment and saves on endless use of aluminum foil or parchment paper. Use it on baking sheets; they come in different sizes and can withstand temperatures of up to 450°. There are many different makes of silicone mats, check them out on Amazon.

Spice Grinder (electric, manual or morter & pestle)

It's not an essential but it's nice to have. Before I had one I used a plastic bag to pound things with my trusty flat meat cleaver. I still use this method for certain things but don't use a coffee grinder; the spices will end up with a coffee scent.

 Spider – Skimmer

It is very useful for fishing things out of very hot liquids. It is a wide mesh, shaped like an open basket and is great for retrieving larger pieces of food or pasta.

 Strainer – Sieve - Chinoise

Is an invaluable tool for filtering unwanted seeds from fruits and vegetables. The chinoise has a very fine mesh and is used for custards, sauces and is sometimes called a China Cap. It is available with a wooden pestle as well, which fits into the cone to extract maximum amount of liquid.

 Toaster oven

It's great for baking or grilling smaller portions. Now that I think of it, I've never used it as a toaster! In the summer months it saves heating up the kitchen with a full size oven.

 **Vegetable Peeler**

Beats the heck out of a paring knife for peeling things!

These are descriptions of a few cooking terms you may not be familiar with.

Beat

Is to use a brisk up-and-down movement to make a mixture smooth.

Caramelize

Is to cook food until its natural sugars are released and it becomes brown in color.

Croutons

Are small pieces of cubed bread that have been browned, either by sautéing, baking or broiling. They are used to garnish soups or salads.

Emulsify

To emulsify means to bind two things together that don't naturally bind, like oil and vinegar. Common emulsifiers include eggs to bind oil and lemon juice for mayonnaise and mustard for vinaigrette.

Dredge

To coat food with flour, corn-meal, breadcrumbs or panko. This coating helps brown the food.

Poach

To poach is to cook food in liquid just below the boiling point. Poached eggs are generally cooked in water and vinegar, fish in white wine, poultry in stock and fruit in wine. Typically an egg is poached in lightly salted water adding a small amount of vinegar to hold the eggs together just to the point where the white is no longer runny and the yolk is beginning to harden around the edges 4 - 5 minutes.

Roux

A roux is a thickening agent using equal parts of fat and flour. The fat is melted in a pot or pan then the flour is added and cooked until the raw flour taste is gone. Color can range from blonde to a dark brown depending on the length of time it is cooked.

Sauté

To cook food quickly in a small amount of oil or other fat in a skillet over relatively high heat. Ingredients are rapidly moved around in the pan, by the using a utensil, or by repeatedly jerking the pan itself. The ingredients are heated at once and cooked quickly.

Slurry

Is a thin paste of water and starch (flour, cornstarch or arrowroot), which is added to hot soups, stews and sauces as a thickener. After the slurry is added, the mixture is typically stirred and cooked for a few minutes in order to thicken and lose any raw taste.

Temper

To heat egg yolks gently by adding a small amount of hot liquid into the yolks and beating well in order to prevent curdling. This term is used for chocolate as well before coating cakes and candies so it remains firm at room temperature.

Index

"The best is yet to be"

Robert Browning

Made in the USA
Columbia, SC
26 July 2018